The autism handbook

Edited by Andrew Nye

Designed by Ian Smythe

Ibis Creative Consultants Ltd

Published by The National Autistic Society

WITHDRAWN

ISBN 1-899280-24-3

045377

Editorial note

The views expressed in this book are those of the individual contributors and do not necessarly represent the policy of The National Autistic Society (NAS).

The NAS does not necessarily endorse the advertisements included in this publication.

While every effort has been made to ensure the accuracy of information given in this handbook, the NAS cannot accept the responsibility for the consequences of any errors or omissions in that information.

In certain articles the masculine pronoun is used purely for the sake of convenience.

First published in Great Britain in 2000 by The National Autistic Society, 393 City Road, London ECIV ING, UK. Registered charity number 269425

Designed and typeset by Ibis Creative Consultants Ltd, 34 Collingwood Road, Sutton SM1 2RZ
☎ 020 8770 0888

Illustrations by Nancy Anderson

Contents

Foreword

Jane Asher, President of The National Autistic Society

I am very pleased to welcome you to the second edition of the Handbook. In this issue we have built on the immense success of the first edition, amending and improving sections in ways based on reactions from readers and adding new chapters.

The original idea behind the Handbook was to bring together in one document information that covered the various needs of all relevant groups: people with autism themselves, parents of children with the disability and professionals working in related disciplines. In this second edition, the Handbook once more offers practical advice on a range of topics, such as pre-school approaches and benefits, and begins with answers to 'frequently asked questions'.

We have added important sections on the transition to further education for students with autism, on options beyond college and on day-to-day living in adult life, including guidance on partnerships, with helpful advice from Brenda Wall of the Asperger Backup Campaign. There is, of course, a practical section giving useful information, such as website addresses, in the gazetteer at the end of the Handbook.

Most importantly, in recognition of the enormous difficulty faced by many in gaining access to vital services, we have included a section called 'Know your rights'. This gives step-by-step guidance on a variety of issues, from getting a diagnosis to help with the assessment and statementing process, from welfare benefits available to contacts for further information.

The National Autistic Society (NAS) was originally set up by parents; their concerns, rights and wishes will always be at the heart of the organisation and guide everything we do. Although there is still a long way to go, I feel far more optimistic now about just what we can achieve for people with autism and their families than I did 12 years ago, when I first began to work with the NAS. We must, however, continue to go from strength to strength, always listening to the views of parents and professionals in order to improve our services, and constantly striving to reach a wider audience.

This Handbook is one more way in which we can work together to support each other. I hope you find it to be as useful and interesting as the first edition was for many people, and I am sure you will join me in thanking all those who have contributed articles to the Handbook and in other ways helped in its production.

Introduction

Andrew Nye, Editor

Welcome to the Handbook 2000. The first edition of the NAS's handbook proved to be a great success and I hope that this edition is equally useful. It is vital that this publication develops as a resource, while retaining the features that everyone finds useful. I hope that this is the case, but please send in any comments and suggestions you have, whether good or bad (new for this edition is a response form on the last two pages of the Handbook, so please fill this in and return it to the Publications Department).

This year we have changed the approach used in the Handbook, with a chronological progression from pre-school to adulthood. The various chapters aim to provide an overview of issues with guidance for further information. Some areas, such as benefits, which are usually dealt with on an individual case-by-case basis, are very complex and could fill hundreds of pages by themselves. Hopefully, however, the pointers given in the Handbook can be used as a basis for accessing further advice and information, and as a handy summary of facts.

As a whole, the NAS has had a busy year since the last Handbook was published. Many projects have developed sucessfully and significantly, such as the pre-vocational skills training 'New Ground' in Wales, the EarlyBird support programme for parents of pre-school children diagnosed with autism, and the 'Diagnostic Interview for Social and Communication Disorders' (DISCO) developed by the NAS and Elliot House.

The successful awareness week in May 1999 helped to raise the issue of how to get a diagnosis. This is very important, as it is the key to accessing appropriate support, education and welfare benefits.

The NAS has also opened a new school in Scotland, Daldorch House, and provision of services in partnership with local authorities and parents continue to form a major part of the NAS's work. Details of these areas, and others, can be found in the Annual Review 1998–99.

A final, and most important, few words. This Handbook would not be possible without the hard work of the many people who have contributed to it, and to the work of the NAS. I would like to thank all of the chapter contributors, the designer Ian Smythe and everyone else who has helped to make it such a success. I look forward to seeing your comments.

What is the autistic spectrum?

An autistic spectrum disorder is a complex developmental disability that affects the way a person communicates and relates to people around them. The autistic spectrum includes the syndromes described by Kanner and Asperger, but is wider than these two subgroups.

The whole spectrum is defined by the presence of impairments affecting social interaction, communication and imagination, usually known as the 'triad of impairments', often accompanied by a narrow, repetitive range of activities.

Other physical or psychological disabilities can occur in association with an autistic spectrum disorder. These include cerebral palsy, Down's syndrome, dyslexia, language disorders and generalised learning disabilities. Epilepsy occurs in about one-third of those with 'typical' autism.

Describing autism

These pin people illustrate some ways in which autism is displayed.

Displays
indifference

Joins in only if adults
insists and assists

One-sided
interaction

Indicates needs by
using an adult's
hand

Lack of
creative
pretend play

Handles or
spins objects

Echolalic – copies
words like parrot

Does not play
with other children

Talks inessantly
about one
subjects

Variety is not
the spice of life

No eye
contact

Bizarre
behaviour

Inappropriate
laughing or
giggling

But some can do some
things very well, very quickly,
but not tasks involving social
understanding

Frequently asked questions

These questions can be downloaded from the NAS website at www.oneworld.org/autism_uk/faqs/faq.html

Diagnosis

I think my child has an autistic spectrum disorder. How do I go about getting them diagnosed?

Autistic spectrum disorders can normally be diagnosed at around the age of 2 years. In many instances professional workers may spot the tell-tale signs of autism via the normal childhood health checks and this will eventually result in them being formally diagnosed.

If this does not happen and you feel that there is a possibility that your child has an autistic spectrum disorder, you should go to your GP and request that they refer your child to a consultant or diagnostic team with a good understanding of the condition.

I have been to my GP but they refuse to refer my child on.

Due perhaps either to financial constraints or lack of knowledge about autistic spectrum disorders, some GPs are unwilling to refer people on. Unfortunately, you have few legal rights in this situation. Under the Patients Charter you can request to see a consultant of your choice or seek a second opinion if you are dissatisfied with the first, but only with the agreement of your GP. However, being assertive and persistent can help. You might also find the following tips useful.

- Prepare notes on what you want to say to your GP prior to your appointment.
- Keep a diary to record any unusual behaviours exhibited by your child and their frequency.

- Supply your GP with some NAS leaflets on autism or encourage them to contact our Information Centre (☎ 020 7903 3599, info@nas.org.uk) if they have any specific questions on the condition.
- If part of a group practice, ask to see one of the other doctors.

Is there a particular kind of doctor that my child needs to see?

There are a number of different doctors and health professionals who may be involved in diagnosing the condition. Most frequently though these would be psychiatrists, clinical psychologists and, in the case of children, paediatricians. In some areas there may be multi-disciplinary teams (i.e. made up of a number of different health professionals) involved in diagnosing autism. It is important to ensure that whoever sees your child has a good knowledge of autistic spectrum disorders.

My GP is willing to refer my child on for a diagnostic assessment but does not know of any people with the relevant expertise.

The Autism Helpline (☎ 0870 600 8585) has a list of doctors and diagnostic teams who have an interest in autistic spectrum disorders and may, therefore, be able to supply you with the name of an appropriately experienced person. We must stress, however, that this list does not offer comprehensive coverage across the country (some areas are better served than others) and we cannot guarantee the service offered by individual doctors or diagnostic teams.

I have heard about The NAS' own diagnostic service, The Centre for Social and Communication Disorders. Would this be the best place to take my child to be diagnosed?

The Centre for Social and Communication Disorders aims to be a centre of expertise and excellence in the field of autism and would be a very appropriate place for someone to go to find out if their child has an autistic spectrum disorder. However, it is not the only option as there are a growing number of health professionals with an interest in the condition, and it is therefore quite possible that there may be someone relatively local to you who could make a diagnosis. If you do see someone local there is the extra benefit that they may be able to advise you on sources of help in the vicinity and possibly offer some kind of follow-up service.

Does everybody with an autistic spectrum disorder need to be diagnosed?

In the experience of the Autism Helpline, very many people with autistic spectrum disorders and their families benefit from having an official diagnosis of their condition. Having an explanation for the problems that the person has been experiencing can bring a sense of relief both for the parent, and sometimes for the person themselves, particularly those at the more able end of the spectrum. It also provides them with the ammunition to argue for the most appropriate services.

There are some occasions where people would prefer not to have a formal diagnosis. Sometimes this is because a parent feels that their child will be able to make greatest progress if they do not think of themselves as having a disability. We also know of adults who suspect that they may be mildly autistic but would prefer not to be formally diagnosed. For such people, knowing what is the possible cause of their problems seems to be enough.

Educational provision

How do I choose the best school for my child with autism?

Autism is a spectrum disorder, which means that parents need to be offered a range of choices to enable them to pick a suitable establishment for their child. The needs and talents, strengths and weaknesses of the individual child must be carefully considered – no one type of school will benefit every child with autism. A range of provisions is required to accommodate the spectrum of need which is present in autistic spectrum disorders.

Will my child be able to attend a mainstream school?

Some children on the autistic spectrum are described as 'high-functioning', 'able' or as having 'Asperger syndrome'. These children may do very well in a mainstream school, in fact they may thrive. Other children can do well in the mainstream setting as long as appropriate support is provided in certain areas. A good example may be the child with Asperger syndrome who performs very well in certain subjects, but finds it very hard to mix with the other pupils socially at playtimes. Therefore, although no academic support is needed, the child may benefit greatly from one-to-one assistance at lesson breaks to help them integrate with their peers (this could take the form of social skills training, speech and language therapy, or arranging for an older pupil to 'buddy' the child – making sure they are not bullied, helping them to understand the rules of games, for example).

What schooling options are there?

Some regions have a wider range of establishments than other areas. Below is a general list, but in order to access detailed information about schools in your locality, you will need to contact your local education authority (LEA).

- Special needs nursery.
- Mainstream nursery.
- Mainstream school.
- Mainstream school with additional support (see statementing section).
- Mainstream school with a specialist unit attached to it (pupils from the unit may integrate with the main body of the school where appropriate, e.g. at playtimes or for certain lessons).
- Speech and language unit (dealing mainly with communication difficulties, perhaps not autism-specific, it may cater for children with a range of learning difficulties).
- School catering for children with severe learning difficulties (SLD).
- School catering for children with moderate learning difficulties (MLD).
- School catering for children with learning difficulties and physical disabilities and/or medical conditions (one-third of children on the autistic spectrum have epilepsy and a child may have a range of conditions overlapping, e.g. autism and cerebral palsy).
- Specialist school dealing solely with pupils on the autistic spectrum.
- Specialist school dealing with a particular part of the spectrum (e.g. Asperger syndrome).
- Specialist school dealing with certain sorts of problems (e.g. children on the spectrum who exhibit challenging behaviours). These establishments may also accept children not on the spectrum with a range of emotional and behavioural problems.
- Alternative schools (e.g. The Sheiling Community, a Rudolf Steiner school).
- Home education. For a variety of reasons some parents decide to teach their children at home. These reasons may include a lack of appropriate provision in a particular area, a suitable short-term solution (e.g. to cover a period of transition between schools) or to allow the family to follow a particular approach (e.g. Lovaas or Option). The NAS has recently begun to compile a register of families involved in home-based schemes, both

to provide a network of support for each other and to allow parents considering this option to discuss the advantages and disadvantages with another parent who has direct experience. For more details about home education please go to the contact addresses at the end of this article.

Please note the above list is not exhaustive, but merely designed to show the range of options available to parents (depending on local provision).

What type of service could the school be?
- Day.
- Weekly boarding.
- Termly boarding.
- Yearly boarding.
- 24-hour curriculum – this refers to a specialist school that offers a complete residential service (incorporating academic studies with independent living and social skills).

Who pays the fees?
Once again, there is a range of possibilities here:
- LEA.
- Parents of the child (if the parental school choice is independently run and the LEA and other agencies refuse to fund the placement).
- Social Services Department (SSD) can sometimes provide funding (this may be in conjunction with the LEA).
- Health Authority may provide funding in certain cases.

Funding may come from a variety of sources (i.e. any of the above) although usually most children will be funded by their LEA.

Are there certain schools that pupils on the spectrum are known to do well at?
Although each child is unique and each placement needs to be viewed individually, certain environments have been found to be useful. Factors to consider when choosing a new school include:
- Is the school well structured? Does it follow a timetable reliably?
- Is there a satisfactory pupil-to-teacher ratio?
- Are there any specialist services, e.g. music therapy, speech and language therapy, a sensory room, a resident educational psychologist? Do you think your child would benefit from this sort of extra curricular activity?

- Is it a large school? (Would your child be able to cope in a big school with a large amount of pupils?)
- Is the school committed to preventing and responding to bullies? Do they have a procedure in place for dealing with these issues; and do you agree with it?
- Does the school have a flexible approach? Would the staff be willing to accommodate any special requirements your child may have? (This may include moving your child up a class for some subjects that they are advanced in, or teaching them in a smaller group situation, or one-to-one for the subjects they have difficulties with.)
- What does the school see as your role? Will they involve you regularly in assessments of your child's progress? Will they inform you of any changes in your child? Will they be willing to work with you to ensure your child can reach their potential?
- Will all members of staff be able to recognise your child and be aware of the way they need to communicate with them effectively (this will be hard to achieve in a large school)?
- Are the teachers aware of, or would they be willing to learn about, the special educational needs of the pupil on the autistic spectrum?
- Do you feel you could approach the Special Education Needs Co-ordinator (SENCO) at the prospective school? Have they played an active role in the statementing procedure for other pupils with special needs? Do they appear well informed, enthusiastic? What do other parents think of them?
- Would your child be explicitly informed of all the school rules? (Some schools appear to have an 'unwritten code of conduct' which children are just expected to know, or to learn from others; the autistic child may find it hard to pick this up.)
- When you visit the school, try to visualise how your child would respond to that environment: will it suit them?
- Would your child be fully assessed on starting the new school?
- Does the school follow a particular approach? Do you agree with the principles of the particular approach? Do they use a range of approaches and models to get the best from your child, or do they try to fit your child in to one rigid model?

How can I obtain information on schools that accept children with an autistic spectrum disorder?

The NAS publishes a list of all schools specifically designed for children with autistic spectrum disorders which are part of its Accreditation Programme. The purpose of the Programme is to ensure that every person with autism receives support in a service that meets national standards, confirming that it understands the nature of autism and is responding effectively and appropriately to the specific needs of people with autism.

The NAS is also aware of other schools which are not part of the Accreditation Programme, but who have stated that they accept children with autistic spectrum disorders. Details of these schools can be found in the publication *Schools, units and classes* (NAS 1998), and from the Information Centre or website.

Who can help me further?

If you are a parent who would like to discuss any educational matters, would like some advice, or would simply like to talk to someone about your concerns, you could contact the Autism Helpline directly. The Helpline can provide you with details of your local autistic society, as well as any nearby parent support groups. Details of the NAS branches and local societies can be found in the Handbook. As these branches and groups will be largely made up of parents, they will have a large body of experience and information about education issues.

For details of useful organisations, official publications, handbooks and guides please refer to the factsheet *Education legislation: a guide to resources (England and Wales)*. If you wish to read some books which address the specific educational implications of teaching autistic pupils, you may wish to refer to the education section of the NAS publications catalogue and the online resource list *The education of children with autism: a selective guide to resources.*

Wills

Information here is taken from the NAS booklet *Making a will: a simple and straightforard guide for families*, available from the NAS Fundraising department on ☎ 020 7903 3753.

What's so special about making a will if you have a dependant who has autism or other learning disabilities?

Parents of people with autism (or other learning disabilityies) need specialist advice on how to prepare a will for the future of their son or daughter. They should seek advice from a solicitor who specialises in this area, as it can be more complex than standard will-writing.

The key difference is that passing on large sums of money to children normally relies on the fact they will become responsible enough to manage their own finances. In the case of children (or adults) who have a learning disability, they may never be in a position to handle their own financial affairs.

Therefore, many parents consider putting their money into a special account managed by people they trust (a trust fund), to ensure their child with autism (or other learning disability) will receive a fair share of inheritance but will have any money 'managed' to the best advantage.

However, there is a further difficulty. Parents are often concerned that their child's right to statutory funding from the Department of Social Security or their Local Authority will be lost if their son or daughter receives a substantial sum of money from their will. This could involve a 'means testing' where the inherited money would count as personal wealth owned by the person with the disability.

Such parents want to ensure that money left by them is used to provide extras for their children, not to replace state funding for the cost of care. Many parents are also anxious that the burden of responsibility for their son or daughter with autism does not automatically go to their other children or relatives. They wish instead to ensure that the lifestyle of all their family is preserved after they have gone, while still ensuring there is adequate and safe provision for their dependant with autism.

These are some of the issues you should consider as part of your will.

1. You will need to appoint one or two responsible people who will ensure that your wishes (through your will) will be carried out appropriately. These people are known as 'executors'.

2. If you have children under the age of 18 years, you should appoint guardians who will take responsibility for them until they become adults. If you have a child with a particular disability this becomes even more important, as their special needs will often create greater demands on any guardians you appoint.

3. In leaving money or goods, your first priority should be your immediate family.

4. You may wish to look into establishing a trust for your disabled child, rather than leave a single lump sum of money which they may be incapable of managing.

5. If you set up such a trust, you will need to appoint specific people who will manage this money (known as 'trustees').

6. If there are any further wishes you may have with regard to special personal possessions or donations to organisations, you must include clear instructions in your will.

7. To help reduce the effects of Inheritance Tax, many people consider leaving money to a favourite charity rather than hand it over to the government by way of tax.

Establishing a Discretionary Trust

For parents considering the future of their son or daughter with a learning disability, a useful way of providing for that person is through establishing a 'Discretionary Trust'. In simple terms, a trust is a binding arrangement between the owner of property or money and specially nominated people who will hold the property or money 'in trust'. Normally, this means placing it in a special account where it can earn interest. The owner of the money can then specify how, and when, the trustees of the fund can, or should, make payments out of this fund. This can either be from the lump sum or the interest earned from it.

In this way, a child or adult who has autism is relieved from the responsibility of managing large sums of money, while having the opportunity of maintaining a higher standard of living.

It would be the trustees who would make decisions on his or her behalf. Therefore, great consideration should be given as to who will make the best trustees in your particular circumstance.

There are two important elements to consider when appointing trustees: one could be a member of the family or close friend who is likely to be in regular communication with your disabled child and to be aware of his or her needs. One should be a person experienced in managing money and investments and having some business sense; such a person could be a family solicitor or accountant.

You can also stipulate that when the person with autism dies the remaining money left in the trust passes to someone else. Again, you can decide how this is divided up and to whom it should go. Quite often this will be a particular charity involved with the person's disability.

Leaving a lump sum

Alternatively, parents can leave money or property directly to an adult with autism, but if that person has insufficient capacity to deal with it, there is a risk someone may challenge the gift. In this case, the person with autism may only be issued a receipt for it by an administrator called in to look at your will.

It is likely that they will seek the appointment of a 'receiver' through a body called the Court of Protection. A receiver has the power to deal with money on behalf of the person, but with restrictions imposed by the court on the use of the money (or property). The receiver's role is similar to that of the trustees, but he is appointed by the Court and not the parents.

Leaving a legacy to charity

This provides a way for you to help carry on the work of a particular charity, such as the NAS. This is usually a gift of money, but there are other items which can be left in this way. Much of the work of large charities relies heavily on the generosity of people who leave legacies to them.

We are always extremely grateful to people who make a provision in their will to help the work of the NAS. This is an extremely effective way of ensuring the work of the Society continues to help people with autism and their families well into the future.

Gifts of residue

Once all your assets have been ascertained by the executors, the debts, funeral and other expenses paid and any legacies dealt with, there may well still be money left over. This is known as the residue. Your will should indicate who should receive this residue and in what manner. The recipients of this money are known as beneficiaries, they may be relatives, friends or charitable organisations.

How can I get further information?

For parents who would like further information on drawing up a will, please contact the Legacy Department, who will be able to supply you with our will-making booklet. It contains information on drafting and amending your will, and special information on how parents of children with a developmental disability can provide for their children when they have gone.

In addition, we have compiled a list of solicitors who specialise in drawing up wills, some of whom have specialist knowledge of families with developmental and learning disabilities.

Contact the NAS on ☎ 020 7903 3526.

Respite care

What is it?

Respite care is an arrangement whereby someone with a disability and the person who cares for them are given a short-term break from one another. Traditionally, this has been seen as being for the benefit of the carer, but increasingly it is being accepted as beneficial for the person with the disability as well.

Where does it take place?
Respite care can be provided either at home or in a residential setting.

How do I ask for it?
In normal circumstances you should contact your local SSD. A need for respite care can be identified via an assessment under the Children's Act 1989, the NHS and Community Care Act 1990 or the Carers (Recognition and Services) Act 1995.

Is it available to people with autistic spectrum disorders and their carers?
Yes, but unfortunately it has to be acknowledged that respite care is a service that is generally in short supply and that people with autistic spectrum disorders are a group for whom it is often difficult to find places within respite services.

What should I do if I am denied respite care or I am unhappy with the service currently being provided?
In the first instance you should utilise your SSD's complaints procedure. All SSDs must have a complaints procedure and, if requested, inform you of how it operates. If this is unsuccessful you may be able to take your case to the Local Government Ombudsman or even possibly the Secretary of State.

Are there any respite care services specifically for people with autistic spectrum disorders?
At present there is only one residential respite service which is specifically designed for people with autism, which is run by The Scottish Society for Autistic Children. However, there is no reason why, with appropriate preparation and training of staff, existing respite services should not meet the needs of people with autism.

Does the NAS offer any kind of respite care service?
Through its Volunteering Network, the NAS is developing a range of Befriending schemes around the country. At present there are schemes in London, Bedfordshire, Leicestershire, Sheffield, Nottingham, Manchester,

Crewe, Chester, Bath, Bristol, Belfast, the Isle of Wight, Cardiff, Glasgow, Swansea, Neath and Port Talbot. Specially selected and trained volunteer befrienders are allocated to individual families and can help in the following ways:

- Supporting the family during leisure activities.
- Taking part in recreational and learning activities.
- Spending time listening and talking to family members.
- Offering temporary respite.
- Going on holiday.

All of us can benefit from going on holiday and this can be the same for people with autistic spectrum disorders and their families. Finding a holiday scheme able to meet their needs can be difficult though. The NAS produces a factsheet which lists a number of holiday schemes that are willing to accept people with autism. It also provides details of useful organisations, some of which can provide practical or financial assistance so as to help people with disabilities and their families go on holiday. To obtain a copy of this publication contact the Autism Helpline or visit the website.

Therapies

What therapies are available for treating people with autistic spectrum disorders?

There is wide ranging opinion as to the best way of treating people with autism, some approaches being based on very specific theoretical views as to the possible causes of the condition.

To help people find out what is available, the NAS publishes an annotated list of over 40 of the most popular and influential approaches in use at the moment. *Approaches to autism* costs £4.50 from the NAS Publications Department.

The NAS Information Centre is also developing a number of factsheets on the various therapies.

Can the NAS recommend any specific approaches?

The NAS will not normally possible make recommendations as to the effectiveness of individual therapeutic approaches. While the organisation appreciates the eagerness of parents to try out new treatments, it feels that any new approach must be fully scientifically evaluated so as to ensure that there are no undesirable side-effects. The policy of the Autism Helpline is to provide an impartial service. Therefore, when approached by someone interested in a particular therapy, its' aim is to provide as much information as possible, hopefully enabling them to form their own opinion.

In many instances there are special interest groups promoting particular approaches and, where appropriate, their details can be passed on to enquirers.

Services for adults

What services are available to adults with autism?

A large proportion of adults with autism will continue to require some degree of support throughout their lives. This could be in the areas of further or higher education, accommodation or health needs. Due to the breadth of the autistic spectrum, the kind of help required will vary enormously. For some this may mean occasional support and guidance in order to help them lead an independent life in the community, whilst for others it may mean full-time support in a staffed home.

How can services be obtained for an adult with autism?

Under the NHS and Community Care Act 1990 all people with special needs are entitled to an individual community care plan, which should be made in consultation with the individual themselves and, where appropriate, their carers. A community care plan should consider all the needs of the person, including: accommodation, health care, education, employment and their social needs.

What should I do if services are refused or I disagree with the service that is offered?

In the first instance you should utilise your SSD's complaints procedure and go from there, as discussed above. If all else fails you may be able to take the SSD to court by requesting a judicial review. Before taking such a step you would need to seek specialist legal advice.

How can I obtain information on services that are specifically for people with autistic spectrum disorders?

The NAS publishes a list of establishments for adults, consisting of all services specifically designed for people with autistic spectrum disorders which are part of its Accreditation Programme.

Welfare benefits

Am I or the person I care for entitled to welfare benefits?

There are a range of welfare benefits available to people with disabilities and many of those with autistic spectrum disorders and their families may be entitled to claim them. Which benefits a person may be entitled to and the amount they can claim will depend on the degree of severity of autism and their individual circumstances. These are all covered in the Handbook section 'Know your rights'.

Other sources of financial help

There is an enormous range of charitable organisations that you may be able to approach for a one-off grant. They vary greatly, both in terms of the level of funding they can provide and their eligibility criteria. Some may only be open to people who live in a particular geographical region, others to those who have been employed in a particular profession. A useful reference book to consult if you are looking for this kind of financial help is *A guide to grants for individuals in need*, edited by David Casson and Paul Brown (Directory of Social Change 1997, ISBN 0907164862). You may be able to find a copy of this in the reference section of your local library.

Further help

Further information and guidance on claiming welfare benefits can be obtained by contacting your local Citizens Advice Bureau, Welfare Rights Unit (address in the phone book), The Disability Alliance or the Disability Benefit Enquiry Line (BEL) ☎ 0800 882200 (Monday to Friday 8.30 am - 6.30 pm and Saturday 9 am - 1 pm).

The Ferret Information Systems Ltd website includes a benefits calculator, latest benefits news section and easy links to other sites http://www.ferret.co.uk/

Further education opportunities

What further education opportunities are there for young people with autistic spectrum disorders?

There is a range of further education options available for young people with autistic spectrum disorders. Depending on their ability, some may be able to access mainstream services, possibly with additional help, whilst others will require courses specifically designed for those with special needs. Further education may take place either within a school or at a college.

At present there are only a handful of further education courses specifically for people with autistic spectrum disorders. The NAS operates an accreditation programme for organisations running autism-specific services, and should be able to provide details of those within the programme that offer further education. Further information on the Autism Services Accreditation Programme is available from the NAS Autism Accreditation Programme, 236 Henleaze Road, Bristol BS9 4NG, ☎ 0117 987 2575.

For further information on further education services in your area it might be worth talking to the Careers Service, an educational psychologist or any local college.

To find out more about colleges nationwide, which whilst not being specifically for people with autistic spectrum disorders may nevertheless be able to meet their needs, the following directories may be helpful.

- *COPE – A Compendium of post-16 education and training in residential establishments for young people with special needs*, compiled by Lynne Gill, Wiltshire Careers Guidance Services, County Careers Centre, Bythesea Road, Trowbridge BA14 8EZ, ISBN 1873408-862.
- *NATSPEC (The Association of National Specialist Colleges).* Directory copies available from Olive Ralphes, Trenor Villa, School Lane, St Martins, Oswestry, Shropshire SY11 3BX, ISBN 0952991705.
- *A London-wide directory of specially designed courses in further education for people with a learning disability*, Mencap London Division, 115 Golden Lane, London EC1Y 0TJ.
- *A London-wide directory of opportunities in adult education for people with a learning disability*, Mencap London Division, 115 Golden Lane, London EC1Y 0TJ.

- *Directory of opportunities for school leavers with disabilities*, Queen Elizabeth's Foundation for Disabled People, Leatherhead Court, Leatherhead, Surrey KT22 0BN, ☎ 01372 842204.
- A more general book that might be useful for young people with disabilities at this stage in their life is *After age 16 - what next?*, The Family Fund, PO Box 50, York YO1 2ZX, ☎ 01904 621115. Free to people with disabilities and their carers.

What happens if my son/daughter has a statement of special educational needs (SEN)?

If your son or daughter is 16 or over and has a statement, the LEA is obliged to continue providing education for them under the terms of the statement. However, once they leave school the statement becomes invalid. If they enter further education ultimate responsibility for their education will lie with the Further Education Funding Council (FEFC). Note though that all young people are entitled to full-time education up until the age of 19.

How does my son/daughter obtain funding for a further education course?

If they are 16 or under an assessment should be carried out by the LEA. If this recommends that they would benefit from a placement in a specialist establisment (known as an out-of-sector placement), their recommendations will be passed on to the FEFC for consideration.

If someone has already left school and is currently out of the educational system an application can be made directly to the FEFC's nearest regional office.

What happens if a funding application for a further education placement is refused?

If an application for a placement is refused by the FEFC you can ask for them to review the decision. If they abide by their original decision you can ask for a review to be carried out by an independent panel.

Will my son/daughter be able to get additional help in college if they need it?

Colleges should have funds available to provide additional support for students with special needs. This issue can be addressed when they are assessed for a place at the college or once they have started the course if necessary. It may be useful to talk to the person at the college with special responsibility for students with disabilities (known either as a learning support co-ordinator or disability co-ordinator).

I don't feel that the staff at my son/daughter's college know enough about autistic spectrum disorders.

The NAS produces and distributes a wide range of literature on autistic spectrum disorders, including information on educational approaches for people with the condition. Further education staff requiring information on autistic spectrum disorders should contact the NAS Information Centre.

For staff working specifically with students with Asperger Syndrome, the Autism Helpline has produced a factsheet *Guidelines for teaching staff at Further Education Colleges teaching Students with Asperger syndrome.*

Useful organisations

The Further Education Funding Council, Cheylesmore House, Quinton Road, Coventry CV1 2WT, ☎ 01203 863000.

Skill: The National Bureau for Students with Disabilities, Charter House, 18-26 Crucifix Lane, London SE1 3JW, ☎ 0800 328 5050, minicom 02800 068 2422, fax 020 72747840; Information Service minicom 020 7978 9890 (weekdays, 1.30 - 4.30 pm), fax 020 7450 0650.

The Advisory Centre for Education (ACE), 1B Aberdeen Studios, 22-24 Highbury Grove, London N5 2EA, ☎ 020 7354 8318, Advice Line: 020 7354 8321 (weekdays, 2 - 5 pm).

Counselling

The term 'counselling' is used throughout and should be seen to incorporate counselling and psychotherapy.

Most parents seek counselling when their sons and daughters reach teenage years. Adolescence can be a traumatic time for anyone – there are so many changes (both physically, hormonally and also in terms of what people expect of you) that this can be a difficult period.

Counselling is rarely an option that immediately springs to mind for individuals on the autistic spectrum, perhaps as part of a backlash against the outdated psychogenic view of autism. Thankfully, thinking has moved on, and the belief in a biological basis for autism has rightfully removed blame from parents and their styles of upbringing. However, despite this shift, for many the clearest association is still with psychoanalytic methods of therapy. No individual method of therapy which persists in seeing the cause of autism as psychogenic is recommended. However, a psychoanalytic approach is only one method within a huge range of counselling options available.

Why seek counselling?

The added complication that autistic spectrum disorders bring to an already awkward time can lead the young to despair. Sometimes depression can lead to suicidal thoughts, self harm, aggression towards others, and an increased reliance on rituals, routines and obsessive behaviours. It is easy to see why events can reach this stage – the individual's communication problems may mean they have never had a true friend, or been able to maintain a healthy relationship. This may be particularly frustrating for very able individuals who are extremely aware of their differences and the problems they have compared to their unaffected peers and siblings. Whereas a child before puberty may be a bit more 'thick-skinned' towards rejections and failures in social interactions, a teenager will be particularly sensitive about not 'fitting in with the crowd'. Whereas parents can intervene with a younger offspring (arrange for them to join scouts/brownies, activity groups etc.), the intense need for the adolescent to be 'cool' and independent can prevent parental input. Understandably, the thought of professional guidance (from an independent expert, i.e. someone who is not a family member or friend, and therefore not on anyone's 'side') can be appealing to both parents and the adolescent.

It is important to acknowledge that some of the problems parents experience with adolescents with autistic spectrum disorders are normal. It is only in rare cases that the teenage years pass smoothly and effortlessly; arguments, screaming matches and "I hate you, wish I'd never been born..." accusations are more usual scenarios for the majority of families. It is important to acknowledge this and not to account for all problems through the autistic spectrum disorder. The individual personality of your particular child will determine a lot.

What sort of features may be seen in the individual with autistic spectrum disorders who has emotional problems?

There are a number of symptoms of negative thought patterns which affect both people on the autistic spectrum and those experiencing anxiety and depression who do not have autistic spectrum disorders:

- All-or-nothing thinking (e.g. I must be OK all of the time without exception).
- Polarised thinking (e.g. people are either my best friend or worst enemy).
- Fatalistic thinking (e.g. things will be bad whatever I do).
- Inaccurate attributions (e.g. my problems are entirely someone else's fault).
- Discounting of evidence if it disconfirms beliefs about the self.

(Taken from *Guidelines for developing working relationships with people with Asperger's syndrome*, Hare 1997.)

Will professional counselling or psychotherapy help?

Firstly, there are some differences in two main areas; the difference between counselling and psychotherapy, and the difference between professional and non-professional help. The differences between counselling and psychotherapy are not always clear.

Counsellors and psychotherapists both work through the therapeutic relationship and both may have similar aims. However, the two disciplines are not the same. Psychotherapy can be said to work on a 'deeper' level, since it deals with issues which may be painful or repressed and so may take some time to deal with as new complications arise. The psychotherapeutic relationship also tends to be more formal, as such issues, by definition, are hard to address outside a mutually agreed and binding professional relationship (especially if the person being counselled is in denial – in which case they may accept more from a professional who is removed from their everyday life and officially in a position of authority). This is not to imply that counselling skims the surface, or only deals with superficial problems, as it may cover very similar issues to psychotherapy. Counselling in some cases can be brief, whereas a bigger commitment may be required from a client undergoing psychotherapy (and also from the psychotherapist).

There are also numerous similiarities between professional and non-professional help. Many people may have the experience of informally counselling friends, family or people in the workplace, although it may not be recognised as such (similarly, a family member who cared for a sick relative was not, until relatively recently, recognised as a carer). In some instances, supportive friendships and a strong social network can sometimes replace the need for professional counselling. It is fair to say that it is harder to informally act as a psychotherapist (as opposed to a counsellor), for the reasons outlined above.

Despite these observations about the crossover between formal and informal counselling, there are important differences that separate a professional relationship from a friendship. These include (Hare 1997):

- Professional relationship.
- Friendship.
- Empathy and (mutual) respect.
- Affection.
- Different backgrounds and interests.
- Similar background and interests.
- Problem-solving focus.
- Emotional/experiential focus.

This section gives only a very brief account; it is impossible to advocate one form of help over another, as each case must be decided on its own merits, and should also take into consideration what options are available in the local area (e.g. it may be hard in some areas to find a psychoanalytic psychotherapist working in the NHS, whereas a client who can afford to go privately may not have this problem).

Professional input may be the only way that some people on the spectrum can receive counselling or similar patterns of help. The difficulties experienced by the person on the spectrum may mean that they do not have a close communicative relationship with family or friends, and therefore cannot rely on these friendships for guidance and support. If there are friends and family who can offer support, it may only be on a narrow range of 'safe' subjects. This could be the result of a range of factors (i.e. the personalities involved or natural styles of communication employed) obsessions and rituals may also limit interaction. The result may be that the person on the spectrum is extremely isolated.

What sort of counselling?

There is a bewildering array of therapeutic approaches available, including humanist, psychoanalytic, psychodynamic, transpersonal, transactional analytic, cognitive, behavioural and gestaltian.

Sometimes a counsellor describes themselves as 'eclectic' which means they use techniques as appropriate to the person or situation, rather than trying to fit the client into one stance. An eclectic approach is not self-explanatory. They do need to elaborate further: what was their original training in? What therapy do they use as the foundation for their work? In which situations would they use psychoanalysis etc? Don't be embarrassed to ask for an explanation or leaflet about their service as there are so many jargonistic, overlapping terms that even the professionals themselves must get confused!

"Have you ever heard of Asperger Syndrome?" It may feel strange asking this question as you may assume that anyone with a psychological background would be aware of the condition. Unfortunately, there is a lot of professional ignorance concerning autistic spectrum disorders. It may be that you are the professional in this situation (you are certainly an expert in how it affects your own child). A good test of the suitability of a would-be counsellor is how open they are when you ask the above question. Are they defensive? Do they try and cover up their lack of knowledge by blinding you with psycho-babble? You will probably get a much better level of service from someone who is honest about their degree of understanding (or lack of).

It may be that they come back to you and do not feel they are a suitable choice but at least they are not wasting your time. Finding the right person is the first obstacle.

It is unlikely that you will find someone with the right approach AND knowledge and direct experience of autistic spectrum disorder clients. You will need to be flexible, as the perfect counsellor may not already exist.

Don't feel obliged to accept a service just because it is offered. Try to meet as many counsellors as possible before making your decision. Obviously this may not be possible if the treatment is being provided through the NHS.

If you are paying for the service yourself, however, you tend to be more in control. Even if you are able to choose from a few professionals, however, you may jeopardise your position if you spend too long deliberating, especially if each service has a waiting list. As mentioned previously, there may be certain approaches that are scarce in the NHS but plentiful in the private sector.

However, there is a great range of services (both counselling and psychotherapeutic) available in the NHS, usually through Clinical Psychology Departments (as opposed to Psychiatry Departments). Try to find out which services are available in your particular location.

If you are going privately, is the counsellor willing to provide a one-off session (free?) to see if they are compatible with your child (and with you?)? If they have never worked with autistic spectrum disorders before do not expect a seamless approach immediately. But have they taken the time to read any literature you gave them? Are they applying the theory in the practical setting, or are they reverting to their normal way of counselling (perhaps not suitable for autistic spectrum disorders)? Are they willing to take tips from you (although they are the counselling experts, they could learn a lot about basic communication principles from you)? Does your child like them? Do they like your child? You can have the best counsellor in Britain, but if there is a personality clash the therapeutic relationship cannot work (this is different to the resistance sometimes encountered when the therapist is bringing up painful subjects, or areas that the client does not want to change).

Are there any particular approaches that may not be suitable for a client with autistic spectrum disorders?

The same guidelines used when choosing what school provision would be best for your child are useful here. The most pertinent points may include some of the following issues.

Is it a structured environment? Will the counsellor provide a clear framework for the sessions? Will they explicitly inform your child of what they expect them to do, how they expect them to behave etc? (This may 'go against' some models of therapy where the client leads the sessions, and the therapist has very little directive input.)

Sometimes, it may be necessary for the counsellor to challenge directly the beliefs exhibited by the child and to make questioning specific (e.g. "Tell me what you don't like about xyz" rather than "What's wrong?"), focusing on explanations rather than interpretations (e.g. "That happened because of abc" rather than "It looks like because you may have thought abc, which means xyz, then ...").

Will the counsellor draw up a clear contract, stating times of sessions, how long they will last for, for how many weeks, months etc.? This is an important precaution to make sure the person with autistic spectrum disorder does not get too dependent on the sessions, or become too distressed when they end. Is the counsellor flexible enough? A child may only be able to engage for brief sessions of perhaps no longer than 10-20 mins (whereas the traditional duration of a session is usually 50 mins).

Due to social and communication difficulties, a group-based therapy session may not be suitable (this will really depend on the size of the group, who the other participants are etc.). These groups may require insight and empathy skills that do not come easily to the client. A group situation may be successful when the focus is on social skills, breaking down and understanding interaction for example.

Will the counsellor be aware of the language they use? Will they avoid language which demands the client to 'read into what they mean'? Will they avoid sarcasm or metaphors? Are they happy to provide the client with very clear instructions? Do they give the client the opportunity to express confusion, and ask for a sentence to be rephrased? Do they understand that open-ended questions can be very hard for a client with autistic spectrum disorders to answer? Are they prepared to work non-verbally (e.g. by making use of visual material, art, drama)? Are they aware of how pervasive special interests, routines and obsessions can be for clients with autistic spectrum disorders? Do they feel confident about preventing a whole session being taken over with fixations? Can they be assertive and supportive when addressing these problems? It is conceivable that the child could become fixated on their feelings and their condition or even by some aspect of the counsellor (such as the counsellor's gender).

Do they practice a counselling approach which looks to problems and traumas in childhood to explain problems in later life?

This sort of approach may be useful when there are additional issues of bereavement, abuse, bullying etc issues which can be linked back to certain past events. However, it is inappropriate to try and find the 'root' of the problems which are actually caused by the triad of impairments (and in Asperger syndrome – the triad and the additional characteristics of Asperger's). This kind of approach could make the client feel worse because as there is nothing to be found, they may end with a sense of failure. It may be appropriate in some cases to use models of counselling designed for people who are physically disabled, i.e. helping the client to adapt to a 'damaged' self or body image. These issues are discussed by Dougal Hare in *The use of cognitive-behavioural therapy with people with Asperger syndrome - a case study* (1997).

Forms of therapy that demand a level of insight and empathy may be particularly difficult. These are areas that a client on the spectrum may need particular help with.

Solution-based approaches may be more appropriate. Although they discuss feelings, emotions, significant events and so on, the emphasis is on providing strategies for dealing with problems and changing behaviour patterns that are inappropriate or self-limiting. Some experts work on the basis that constantly talking about experiences (i.e. what happens/what has happened) does not lead to change and may often be a way of avoiding responsibility in life. This may especially be the case for people with Asperger syndrome, due to their tendency to blame other people for their problems. A practical approach may work very well for a child with an autistic spectrum disorder, where the focus is not solely on communicating feelings to the counsellor as much as communicating everyday tasks, goals for the week etc. (i.e. object-centred as opposed to person-centred). Even an expert cognitive-behaviourist counsellor will need to modify their techniques so they are suitable for the child with an autistic spectrum disorder (e.g. behaviour patterns, reassurance behaviours may be harder to give up/replace than for a client without a autistic spectrum disorders).

Difficulties may arise in counselling with children who persist in seeing their autistic condition as a way of avoiding responsibility and refusing to change.

By seeing the autistic spectrum disorders as the explanation for any difficulties, the individual is exonerating themselves, as if their future is predetermined and nothing they do will have an effect (this ties in with the all-or-nothing thought patterns common in depression). Moving away from the issues of Asperger syndrome and focusing instead on personal life events of the child can help initiate therapeutic contact.

Academic views

Since the early 1990s there has been considerable and growing interest concerning the use of psychotherapeutic work for people with learning disabilities. Various approaches have been discussed ranging from psychodynamic perspectives to those which approach therapy from a more behavioural/cognitive slant. All experts involved are agreed that there is a need to develop more appropriate forms of clinical work with people with an autistic spectrum disorder.

Cognitive-behavioural approaches may be a suitable alternative. The disorder embodies faultless logic and it has been noted that if an approach could maximise upon this natural tendency, results could be promising. In this form of psychotherapeutic work, the emphasis is on the way an individual's behaviour is influenced by both their immediate situation and, just as importantly, by their interpretation of it, rather than focusing on more global and historical factors. Unfortunately, there is not a lot of information available on this approach and the autistic spectrum disorder.

In contrast, there is quite a lot of information with regards to psychoanalysis and autism. Escoffier-Lambiotte (1985) believes that as a twin study indicates the cause of autism is genetic rather than psychogenic, psychoanalysis (although the major treatment trend in France) is little help. Eleven UK psychiatrists back up the author by stating "evidence indicates biological and not social environmental origins for autism". The author concludes "psychoanalysis seems inappropriate for autism, but needs proper study".

Note: psychoanalysis is but one form of psychotherapy – the criticism above concerns this particular form and not psychotherapy in general, which may be effective for some clients.

References

Guidelines for developing working relationships with people with Asperger's syndrome, D. J. Hare, NAS, 1997. (Written when the author was Senior Clinical Psychologist with the NAS.)

Hare, D. J. (1997), *The use of cognitive-behavioural therapy with people with Asperger syndrome: a case study, Autism - The International Journal of Research and Practice*, 1(2).

Hare, D. J. and Paine, C., *Developing cognitive behavioural treatments for people with Asperger's syndrome, Clinical Psychology Forum* 110.

Useful numbers to find a suitable therapist

- The British Association of Counselling
  BAC will provide a list of accredited counsellors working in particular regions across the country, ☎ 01788 550899.

- UK Council for Psychotherapy
  As above UKCP will provide names of psychotherapists working in different areas, ☎ 020 7436 3002.

- British Association for Behavioural and Cognitive Psychotherapies
  BABCP may be similarly useful, will be able to provide a register of professionals specialising in certain areas (e.g. working with children and adolescents) ☎ 01254 875277.

- British Psychological Society.
  BPS maintains an annual register of chartered psychologists. A useful organisation to contact for information and literature ☎ 0116 254 9568.

Cases must be viewed individually and should consider the particular personality involved.

Help for families from overseas

I suspect that my child may have an autistic spectrum disorder. Would it be possible to come to Britain to have them diagnosed?
Unfortunately, it is usually difficult for parents from overseas to do this. Specialist professional knowledge of autistic spectrum disorders is still not as widespread as we would like to see, one of the results being that those doctors who are reliable diagnosticians of the condition tend to have extremely long waiting lists. Furthermore, most of the doctors that we know of work within the National Health Service (NHS), i.e. the state systems and may not therefore be able to accept referrals from overseas. For those parents who are willing to pay we can supply the names of a few doctors we know of who see private patients. However, these again tend to have long waiting lists.

Could I take my child to Britain for therapeutic treatment?
There are very may different approaches for treating children with autistic spectrum disorders, so in asking a question like this it is really necessary to clarify what kind of help you are looking for. Where help is available through the NHS it would probably be extremely difficult for parents from overseas to access this for their children. There are, however, many therapies that are available privately, therefore if you are interested in a particular approach we may be able to supply you with the details of an appropriate practitioner or treatment centre.

Could I send my child to a specialist school in Britain?
There are a range of specialist schools in Britain for children with autistic spectrum disorders which are run either by LEAs, in effect the state, or independent organisations such as ourselves. The great majority of these schools, including the NAS's, do not accept private fee paying pupils. Instead, places are funded by the LEA in which the child lives. In order to be eligible for this funding a child has to have official residential status in Britain. In other words, in most cases it would not be possible for parents to send their child to school in this country if they were not living here themselves. If you would like to check your legal right to settle in Britain, either permanently or for an extended stay, contact the Immigration Advisory Service, County House, 190 Great Dover Street, London SE1 4YB, ☎ 020 7357 6917, fax 020 7378 0665, iasuk@gn.apc.org.

Further issues to bear in mind are that even if a child were to become resident in Britain there would be no guarantee that an LEA would agree to send them to a specialist autistic school or, even if they did agree to this in theory, that there would be a vacancy available for them.

It is also important to remember that all specialist schools for children with autistic spectrum disorders in Britain use English to teach their pupils. Therefore it would be extremely difficult for a child whose first language is not English to benefit from a school in this country.

Could I pay for my child to attend a specialist school in Britain?

As explained above, most specialist schools for children with autistic spectrum disorders do not accept private fee-paying pupils. There are a few that do though and details of these can be found in *Schools, units and classes*, (NAS Publications £2.99).

For those parents willing to consider non-specialist schools (those not specifically for children with autistic spectrum disorders but nevertheless willing to consider pupils with the condition), the following two organisations may prove helpful. Both produce directories of schools willing to accept children with disabilities.

- The Independent Schools Information Service (ISIS), 56 Buckingham Gate, London SW1E 6AG, ☎ 020 7630 8793/4.
- Gabbitas Educational Consultants, Carrington House, 126-130 Regent Street, London WiR 6EE, ☎ 020 7734 0161.

Would it be possible for me to send my child to a specialist school in Britain for a short time only, so as to learn some basic skills?

While it is certainly the case that educational approaches can reduce many of the problems associated with autistic spectrum disorders, this is not something that can usually be achieved in a short space of time.

Can the NAS advise me on the availability of specialist services in my country or my legal rights in asking for such help?

As a national, rather than international organisation, the NAS does not have the resources to collect detailed information on the availability of specialist services for people with autistic spectrum disorders in other parts of the world or legal rights in asking for such help (indeed it is a very hard job just keeping up to date with such issues with regard to the situation in Britain). However, we hold a list of all the national autistic societies that we know of in other parts of the world who may be able to provide this kind of information, and would be happy to let people know whether there is one operating in their country.

Can I obtain general information on autistic spectrum disorders from the NAS?

Yes, we are very happy to supply people in any part of the world with literature to explain more about autistic spectrum disorders. If you would like to receive further information please visit the Enquiry Service area of the website or contact the Information Centre. Alternatively, those directly affected by the condition, such as parents or people who are themselves autistic, could contact the Autism Helpline directly. Interested professionals should contact the NAS Information Centre. Although the NAS cannot advise on the availability of specialist services for people with autistic spectrum disorders in other parts of the world or their legal rights in asking for such help, it will do its' best to answer any more general questions on autism and methods of helping people with the condition.

The publications catalogue contains details of a wide range of useful titles that can be ordered. Some people may also find it useful to join the NAS, which will entitle them to receive our magazine *Communication*, a useful means of keeping in touch with what is going on in the world of autism.

Bullying

How can I protect my child from bullying?

A bully can be anyone: classmate, sibling, your own child, even a teacher. It has been estimated that half a million school children in Britain are being bullied (*Bullying in schools* 1998). Girls and boys use different tactics when bullying; boys are usually physically violent, whereas girls use a psychological approach, singling someone out and ostracising them. Pupils with a disability can be especially vulnerable to bullies, those children who have difficulties 'fitting in' socially with peers can be particularly easy targets. The following tips aim to reduce this unacceptable behaviour.

Talk to your child's teacher about finding a 'buddy'. This could be an older child who keeps an eye out for any trouble involving your child, or a classmate who is mature and friendly. A buddy could also help your child to join in with games (they could explain the rules of a particular activity) as sometimes just by 'standing out' a child can become a target for would-be bullies.

Could your child be helped by the teacher organising a 'circle of friends' for them? The 'circle of friends' approach aims to help children with disabilities to integrate into their peer groups (usually within mainstream schools). As with the buddy schemes, this can help the child to fit in more, which can serve the dual purpose of tackling problem behaviours (which may prevent friendships) and reducing the child's vulnerability to bullying. If you are interested in setting up a circle, please contact the helpline for guidelines.

Notify the school of any worries you have – the lunch-time staff, playground assistants and caretakers could all be made aware of your concerns.

Approach your child's teacher about covering bullying in a lesson. If you feel bullying could be happening in your child's class, approach the form teacher. By arranging a special lesson that confronts this issue directly (without blaming any individuals) the children in the class will be able to learn effective ways of preventing or responding to bullying. Role plays can be very helpful in this kind of situation; by acting out playground scenes (suggested by the children themselves), the class can discuss ways to respond to children they see bullying others, as well as how to react if they themselves are bullied. The children can experience how it feels to be a bully or a victim, as well as what to do if you are a bully but need help to stop. It is essential to inform the child of where to go for help. There may be a particular teacher in the school they can approach about bullying issues; if they have not met this individual they should be introduced. The class can discuss ways to respond to children they see bullying others, as well as how to react if they themselves are bullied. Kidscape run school-based courses with children on self assertion and bullying. They also have a helpline for parents with a child involved with bullying (☎ 020 7730 3300, weekdays 10am - 4pm). They can send out information sheets and publications (enclose an SAE). Contact them at World Trade Centre, Europe House, Box 10, London E1 9AA, ☎ 020 7488 0488.

'Circle of friends'

A group of six to eight children volunteer to form the circle, the 'focus child' (the child having problems) and their family will have already been approached and are in agreement before this stage. The circle arranges with the supervising member of staff to meet on a regular basis (perhaps one lunch time, or after school once a week). The sessions are brief (20 – 40 mins) and members focus on identifying problems, planning practical steps to resolve them, and reviewing any progress which has been made.

When the Leicestershire Autism Outreach Team established seven different circles in 1997, the results were very promising. There appeared to be few (if any) drawbacks for anyone involved. Staff reported a range of benefits for the focus child including:

- Improved social integration and higher levels of peer contact. For the focus child this extended beyond the immediate circle and this was thought to be due to the child's reduced anxiety about social interaction and increased desire for contact.
- Reduced anxiety in the focus child. Teachers described them as 'bubblier', 'happier' and 'more relaxed'.
- Improved behaviour. The group focused on overtly challenging behaviour, or visible routines that disrupted the day, e.g. one focus child engaged in compulsive hair brushing.

Any drawbacks?

Problems did not deteriorate further in any of the focus children. In two of the seven circles, staff mentioned 'increased egocentricity', which ties in with empathy problems evident on the spectrum. When the staff member intervened and brought the needs and feelings of the other circle members to the attention of the focus child, the circles became more of a mutual support network. This happened spontaneously in two other circles.

Did other members of the circle benefit?

Staff reported:

- Increased levels of empathy and improved understanding. The children became good at not taking the focus child's behaviour personally, this reduced their blaming orientation. They became more balanced about their classmate, taking their strengths and weaknesses into account.
- Enhanced self esteem. Staff reported a sense of competence and pride from the circle.
- Improved group participation. This was noticed in three of the seven circles.
- Benefits for individual group members. One child with emotional and behavioural difficulties (not the focus child) changed his teacher's perspective of him, because of the sensitive and enthusiastic participation he displayed in the circle. Another child with similar difficulties showed improved behaviour outside the circle. Two shy children "had begun to find their voices" over the course of the meetings, and were contributing more confidently.

Any drawbacks?

No significant problems. However, in two incidences circle members became distressed when faced with "unexpected and intense reactions" from the focus child in the course of the discussions.

Further reading

For parents/teachers interested in reading the original article:
Children with autism and peer group support: using 'circles of friends', *The British Journal of Special Education* June 1998, 25(2).

For parents/teachers interested in setting up a circle:
Using 'circle of friends' (a peer support strategy) with children with autism, Penny Barratt, Helen Joy, Mo Potter, George Thomas and Philip Whittaker

If your son or daughter uses little or no speech, you will have to develop a system that allows you to communicate about any problems they may be having.

One good way may be to prepare a board with many different faces on it, showing different expressions. If your child cannot verbally tell you about their day, you could ask them to point to the appropriate face (you could even have a 'bully' representation on the board). Children with an autistic spectrum disorder may have particular problems conveying their feelings, so look out for any behavioural changes in your child. Increased anxiety, perhaps a greater insistence on routines, more frequent tantrums, reduction in appetite could be accounted for in a number of ways, but bullying may be one of them.

If your child is able, show them how to dial Childline Freephone ☎ 0800 1111. Make sure they realise that they can ring at any time (it's open 24 hours a day), and if they call from a payphone they will not need any money. Perhaps the number could be displayed in the toilets at school.

What if the bully is a teacher?

Any behaviour of this sort should be reported immediately to the Headteacher, the school governors and, if necessary, the police. A particularly helpful association is the Children's Legal Centre (Advice Line open weekdays, 10am – 12pm and 3 – 5 pm, ☎ 01206 873820, or you could write to them at University of Essex, Wivenhoe Park, Colchester CO4 3SQ, or email: clc@essex.ac.uk) who will be able to advise you about proceedings (including referrals to criminal or civil court agencies). Corporal punishment is illegal, apart from in some independent schools, but even then it must not be 'excessive' or 'improperly motivated'. If your child is in such a school and you do not want your child to be punished in this manner, you should write to the Headteacher, clearly stating your wishes.

Other useful agencies

ACE (Advisory Centre for Education) in association with BBC and Childline have produced *Bullying - a guide for parents*. ACE produce a range of literature concerning bullying, including information sheets for school governors and other staff involved in education. These can be ordered from ACE for the cost of £1; send a SAE to ACE Ltd, 1b Aberdeen Studios,

22 Highbury Grove, London, N5 2EA. ACE also have an advice line – ☎ 020 7354 8321 (Mon to Fri, 2 – 5pm) fax: 020 7354 9069, ace-ed@easynet.co.uk

Anti-Bullying Campaign (ABC) have a telephone helpline offering support and advice to parents, including steps the school and education system can take. Open weekdays 9.30am – 5pm, ☎ 020 7378 1446, 185 Tower Bridge Road, London SE1 2UF, fax: 020 7378 8374.

Publications

There are a number of publications focusing on bullying, which may be useful for both schools and parents, here are a few (a more comprehensive list can be found in the back of the ACE and Childline guide for parents).

Don't pick on me: how to handle bullying, Rosemary Stones, 1993, Piccadilly Press Ltd, 5 Castle Rd, London NW1 8PR, ISBN 1853401595, £5.99.

Bullying at school: what we know and what we can do, Dan Olweus, 1993, Blackwell, 108 Cowley Road, Oxford, OX4 1JF, £8.99.

Bullying: a positive response, advice for parents, governors and staff in schools, Delwyn Tatum and Graham Herbert, 1990, Faculty of Education, South Glamorgan Institute of Higher Education, Cyncoed Road, Cardiff CF2 6XD, £1.25.

Words will really hurt me. How to protect your child from bullying, Martine Ives/Autism Helpline, 1999, NAS Publications, ISBN 1899280162, £1.00.

These are just a few suggestions, but any parents who have had direct experience of bullying problems and would like to suggest some tips, please let us know.

Pre-school approaches

Jane Shields, NAS EarlyBird Centre Manager

Introduction

When an autistic spectrum disorder is diagnosed in a pre-school child, parents may have mixed feelings of grief and frustration. They will need time to adjust to the diagnosis but can be helped by being given up-to-date information about autism and practical help to maximise their child's development. Early intervention is known to help children with a range of developmental disorders, including autism, and the involvement of parents is essential. There has been great interest in early intervention of late and a number of models are becoming available. Some work with and through parents to help their child, e.g. the NAS EarlyBird Programme; some involve the child in home-based intensive programmes, e.g. Lovaas/ABA (Applied Behavioural Analysis) or Options. There are other ways in which parents may choose to help their pre-school child, such as using picture symbols to develop communication, trying a gluten- and/or casein-free diet, or using educational software on a home computer. This chapter presents information about some of these ways to help the pre-school child at home, together with stories from parents who have experienced each approach.

The NAS EarlyBird Programme

In 1997 the NAS set up the EarlyBird Project in South Yorkshire, a pilot project to develop and evaluate a model of early intervention which involves a 3-month parent programme. The pilot project has successfully used the EarlyBird programme with groups of six families at a time and the

accompanying research study has confirmed parents' feelings of being helped by participating in the programme. The EarlyBird Centre has now begun to offer training in the licensed use of the programme and its supporting materials, to teams of autism-experienced professionals from other areas of the country, so that more families can eventually participate.

EarlyBird combines group training sessions for parents with individual home visits, when video feedback is used to help parents apply what they learn when they are working with their child. Parents have a weekly commitment – to a 3-hour training session or a home visit, and to ongoing work with their child at home – during the 3-month long programme. This short-term, focused model of early intervention aims to support parents in the period between diagnosis and school placement, as well as to empower parents. The three strands of the programme help parents to understand their child's autism; to develop their child's social communication; and to establish good practice in handling their child at an early age so as to pre-empt the development of inappropriate behaviours. The content of the NAS EarlyBird Programme is autism-specific, drawing on well established practice and including techniques from the NAS's SPELL approach, Division TEACCH, and from PECS (Picture Exchange Communication System). All professionals licensed to use the programme have had previous experience of working with people with autism. The programme makes extensive use of video, including clips and interviews with other parents of a pre-school child with autism. The children of families participating in the programme do not visit the programme base, but parents are able to 'meet' each other's children on video and share the progress made at home during the programme.

EarlyBird aims to help parents understand why the development and behaviour of their pre-school child with autism may be different, so that parents can go on working out how best to help their child. The rapport and support which develops between each group of six families has proved to be an important component of the programme, which allows parents to learn with and from each other, guided by professional support. Parents who participated in the pilot project were found to be less stressed both at the end of the programme and at a follow-up 6 months later.

Lynne's story

Lynne Gillis – mother of Joseph – describes the benefits she found from participating in EarlyBird

"EarlyBird was a lifeline to me – an oasis of knowledge in the desert of practical solutions to everyday problems.

"Joseph was a difficult baby who demanded constant attention and grew into a very self-directed toddler. He would not eat, sleep or comply with any requests and would only communicate his own needs. Tantrums were frequent, long-lasting, loud and physical. Our whole life was run on his terms. I was ashamed of my son and my own abilities as a mother. I lost all confidence in myself in every aspect of my life. I felt a total failure. Relationships suffered, particularly with my husband and mother.

"The EarlyBird Programme gave me the knowledge, skills and understanding of my son's behaviour to start to regain control of my life. I am now able to help Joseph in many different ways and will continue to use the techniques for years to come.

"A few months after EarlyBird finished I suddenly realised that at last I was beginning to enjoy motherhood, I actually liked my child and was very proud of his achievements.

"I should like to say a great big thank you to the NAS, and particularly Jane and Glenis for giving me the confidence and power to regain control of my life. I have learned to laugh again!"

LOVAAS/ABA

The LOVAAS method is an early intensive behaviour therapy approach for children with autism and other related disorders. It is also known as the UCLA (University of California Los Angeles) Model of Applied Behavioral Analysis (ABA). It is based on extensive American clinical experience and research carried out over more than 30 years by Ivar Lovaas.

Lovaas and his colleagues recommend that treatment should begin as early as possible, preferably before the child is 5 years old and, ideally, before the child reaches 3¹/₂ years. This is necessary in order to teach basic social, educational and daily life skills. It can also reduce stereotypical and disruptive behaviours before they are established. The home-based programme consists of 40 hours per week of intensive therapy. Results of Lovaas' studies show the importance of maintaining these hours in order to maximise the benefits to the child.

The therapy is on a one-to-one basis for 6 - 8 hours a day, 5 - 7 days a week for 2 years or more. Teaching sessions usually last 2 - 3 hours without a break. The intensity of the therapy means that there is usually a need to establish a 'programme team' which normally consists of at least three persons. These people have all undergone a full training programme. All skills are broken down into small tasks, which are achievable and taught in a very structured manner, accompanied by lots of praise and reinforcement. Examples of re-inforcers are small bites of food, play with a favourite toy and social rewards such as verbal praise, hugs and tickles.

The intervention programme progresses very gradually from teaching basic self-help and language skills, to teaching non-verbal and verbal imitation skills, and establishing the beginnings of toy play. Once the child has mastered basic tasks the second stage teaches expressive and early abstract language and interactive play with peers. In more advanced stages of intervention the child can be taught at home and school.

Lovaas and his colleagues believe that with early intervention a sizeable minority of children (just under 50%) with autism and related disorders are able to achieve normal educational and intellectual functioning by the age of 7 years. For those children who do not achieve normal functioning it is claimed there are usually substantial decreases in inappropriate behaviours and acquisition of basic language is achieved. There is continuing discussion as to the validity of Lovaas' findings. The treatment is extremely long and intensive and can therefore prove to be very expensive. However, a growing number of parents have used this method and have been pleased with the results.

Deb's story

Deb McDougall – mother of Jamie – describes what she got from the programme and what it meant for her son

"At EarlyBird I learned a great deal about autism and how to cope and live with the day-to-day problems that arise from this condition. It gave me hope and inspiration and confidence in myself and my son. It taught me how to see into my child's mind and understand the underlying causes of some of the symptoms.

"I learned how to play with my son and through play to set up social routines and eventually how to get my son talking. I learned about 'PECS' and I am now using this with my son and it has helped language to develop.

"I am less stressed and can cope better. As a result my son is much happier (because I am!) and other people have commented on this.

"My son has started talking, albeit very early stages, but what is encouraging is that on the rare occasion that he uses language it is in context and with meaning. His eye contact and social contact have improved no end and this has been noticed by other people, including his nursery teachers, bus escort, etc.

"My friend, who also has a little boy with autism, has noticed a difference in me since I attended EarlyBird. She says I have improved no end and seem much more in control and cope with things much better than when we first met. She says I was panicking about Jamie's autism and what to do about it then, but now I have a much better understanding of his condition – I seem much less stressed than I was before. My friend has noticed that EarlyBird is not a therapy like Lovaas but more a parent education and stress relieving course, which arms parents with day-to-day coping strategies and information on more practical therapies and techniques."

Diane's story

Diane Fellows – mother of Oliver – describes the ups and downs of running a Lovaas style home based programme

"I am the mother of Oliver, a 3$^{1}/_{2}$ year-old boy whom we were always led to believe had severe autism. We now know that Oliver's autism is only moderate but he did have severe compliance problems as well.

"We have recently started a Lovaas or ABA home-based therapy programme and do about 30 hours a week. This has tackled his compliance and his autism and Oliver is now steadily overcoming both. Whilst I would not say that Lovaas is a miracle cure, I would say that it has helped improve our quality of life enormously.

"Oliver will now respond to his name, come when asked, sit down when asked and he is generally more 'in our world'. He is more compliant in every aspect of his life and is learning so fast that we are struggling to keep up with him. We have been astonished by how bright he is.

"The down-side is that we are having to pay specialist therapists, charging £5 an hour plus travelling time. We have a supervisor who comes fortnightly and is £70 for half a day, but she does ring us for an hour in the week that we don't see her so that she can move the programme along and iron out our problems. She is always available 24 hours a day! We also use a Norwegian consultant who will come to us four times a year and do a one day workshop each time - roughly £1000 per visit.

"Then there is the cost of building a special room which is Oliver's work room. We built a conservatory and kitted it out for him, at a cost of £10,000. We also have to buy new toys, books, puzzles and rewards weekly at a cost of around £30.

"It is quite intrusive into your lives – we have strangers in our home for 30 hours a week. We believe it is worth it. Our little boy is definitely improving considerably."

Pre-School

The Option Institute's Son-Rise Program

This Program uses an interactive approach to early intervention emphasising the importance of developing a relationship and communication between the child and its parents. The programme is child-centred: the child is not judged and their behaviours are not seen as good or bad, rather the child is seen to be doing the best he/she can.

The Option method developed from the efforts of Barry and Samahria Kaufman to help their autistic son, Raun. The Kaufmans designed and implemented a home-based programme for Raun, and later published their experiences, which were also made into a film, Son-Rise, A Miracle of Love. As interest grew, in 1983 they established the Option Institute and Fellowship in the United States. The Option Institute offers training programmes for families with special children, using the methods originated by the Kaufmans and taught under their supervision.

The Son-Rise philosophy encourages the parent (or instructor, therapist or facilitator) to become the student of the child's world, observing, learning, assisting and supporting the child's developing in a loving and non-judgemental environment. The child becomes the teacher, guiding the process, discovering and exploring self and the world. This approach of 'going with' the child, rather than against, helps the child to become more motivated to explore and develop. Many of the ideas used in this approach can be seen in parallel principles which underlie the procedures of behavioural intervention, especially those used in gentle teaching.

Parents are trained, and then set up and manage the programme at home. The use of a therapy room, designed to offer as little distraction as possible, is recommended. The therapy room should have diffusers on the windows, a diffused artificial light source and only one adult working with the child at any one time. These measures are designed to filter out distractions and help the child to concentrate. Materials are placed out of reach of the child and can only be obtained by the child through communication with the adult. The Option approach emphasises imitation, based on research showing that an adult imitating the actions of a child increases the eye contact between the two and develops the use of creative play.

Andrea's story

Andrea Spinks – mother of Emily – describes their Option based home programme

"Since February 1998 I have been working with Emily for 2$^1/_2$ hours each morning on an Option based programme. She has also had one-to-one tuition from Hilary since June 1998, taking her hourly 'therapy' to 4$^1/_2$ a day. We began working with Emily on her second birthday, she is now almost 3$^1/_2$ years old.

"The Options idea is based in working with your child on their terms but being careful to set goals and achieve the desired outcomes without confrontation. It basically suggests that to accept and work well with your child you must initially understand them so completely that you try to get into their world. It is more to do with the simple idea of working from their side towards ours rather than forcing a world of terms and conditions upon people to whom it simply makes no sense. I was surprised at how, given time, it is possible to read situations through your child's senses if you are present with them on this one-to-one basis.

"All the time we spend with Emily is in a room that we have made to the Options specifications. This is a converted bedroom with blank walls, a lino floor, a few shelves out of reach with toys on and large mirrors. This blankness enables Emily's concentration levels and eye contact to rise to a much higher pitch than in any other environment. There is nothing to distract her, nothing to filter out - just you, the child and the endless possibilities of communication. It really is good fun! The only stimulating thing about this environment will be you.

"Emily's autism, we feel, is quite severe. She has very little language and I suspect no receptive language as yet. However, she continues to make remarkable progress in this learning environment and her concentration level and eye contact have vastly improved, thus giving her an opportunity to learn.

"Emily is more happy and confident than we could have imagined at this stage in her development. Her sociability is remarkable and she now mixes very well with her peers as well as adults. She has developed many self-help skills and a very real ability to use her learned imagination in extremely appropriate ways. Eighteen months ago Emily was totally self-absorbed, swaying and staring into space with a fixation about dummies. Due to these incredible changes in her trust in people, none of these traits exist in her any more. I strongly believe that the one-to-one child led therapy has suited our family and provided Emily with a very real and permanent foundation on which to build her millions of potential goals and achievements."

The Option Institute offers a 1-week programme which it says "provides a customised/individualised training, which enables families to return home and direct a successful Son-Rise Program". Additional advanced training and return weeks are available. The Institute recommends that both parents of the child attend the course or if this is not possible a close relative, friend or other support person.

Using picture symbols (including PECS)

Children with an autistic spectrum disorder have difficulty understanding the world around them, especially other people. They have difficulties with social communication and many are slow to develop the understanding and use of spoken language. Their 'mind-blindness' increases their problems in figuring out how communication works; if you lack the understanding that another person may not know what you want, why make the effort to communicate that want? Similarly, their restricted understanding of spoken language, and of time sequences, can limit their ability to cope with the sequences of daily routines such as getting up, dressing, going shopping, or going to bed. Since people with autism are visual learners, many of these confusions can be helped by visual communication methods, such as the use of picture symbols.

The Picture Exchange Communication System (PECS) was developed in Delaware USA, in 1987, by Frost and Bondy, to help young children with autism learn to initiate requests and communicate their needs. PECS uses a behaviourally based programme to teach the child to exchange a picture card for something the child likes and wants. Objects, pictures or symbols may be used, according to the child's developmental level, but many young children with autism find the less detailed line drawing of a symbol easier to understand, especially if this is accompanied by the written word. A picture cut out from a certain packet of crisps may be refused by the child with autism for use with any other type (or brand!), whereas the more general outline of a symbol will be accepted as referring to all 'crisps'. PECS first assesses the child's preferences, for a small number of food items and some toys. The child is then taught, in a carefully graded pattern of small steps, to exchange a symbol representing one of these wanted items for the item itself.

At first two adults are needed so that the child can be physically, but not verbally, prompted to exchange the symbol, rather than grab the wanted item. One item, and its symbol, is worked on at a time. No verbal prompts are given; the first speech the child hears will be the name of the item, said by the adult offering it, as the exchange is made. The second adult stands behind the child, offering a physical prompt to encourage the child to exchange the symbol, but never speaking. Once the child learns to give the symbol, this second adult is no longer needed.

The six phases of PECS are carefully structured to enable the child to learn the picture exchange, to actively find someone to give a symbol to as a request, to discriminate between several symbols, to use a portable communication book, and to construct simple sentences, both requests and comments. The child gradually becomes independent of adult prompting and learns that communication is a two-way process which can achieve desired needs. PECS has been shown to facilitate the development of spoken words and establishes the basics of communication in advance of the hoped-for emergence of speech.

Children learn to communicate with PECS because they are highly motivated to request a wanted item and because PECS teaches visually explicit skills, using only physical prompts which can be gradually faded, thus avoiding the child becoming prompt-dependent. PECS is easy to use and does not involve expensive equipment, testing or training, although training courses for professionals are available, together with a video.

PECS helps pre-verbal children with autism learn how to express their needs, about how communication works. Children who can already speak may also benefit from the use of picture symbols to help them understand the sequence of daily routines. Using pictures in this way can prevent tantrums and encourage the development of independence in self-help skills such as dressing. Symbols can also be used to help the child understand available

Judith's story

Judith Betchette – mother of James aged 3½ – describes the progress he is making with communication following the introduction of PECS

"James, at the age of 3 years and 1 month, was still non-verbal. He communicated by leading us by the hand to where the item was he wanted, normally food, at which point we would take out what we thought he wanted, make him point to his choice and then give him the item in question. This was our sole method of communication.

"We started gradually with PECS with one picture at first – an apple. James loves these and food has always been a great motivator with him. The first time I tried it was with my mother as the 'silent prompter' - no joy! "Maybe he's tired" was our thought; it was an afternoon and he had been to nursery that morning. So the next day I tried it again with James' Special Needs Assistant as the prompter. We haven't looked back since.

"James now has three pictures stuck with velcro on the front of a folder and we are in the process of building up a bank of other pictures for him to use. We have been lucky – my brother is a graphic designer and he is supplying the pictures for me, but I am also busy contacting James' speech therapist and outreach to see if they can help as I do not like imposing on him in such a way.

"For us, as a family, this has been a major breakthrough in communication with James. It has started to remove the uncertainty and replaced it with a sense of pride in seeing James communicate with us and our understanding him."

choices, or to reinforce the concept that something is 'finished' and show the child what will happen next. This use of 'visual structure' is part of the TEACCH approach and can be used at home, as well as at school.

Pre-School

Diet modifications

It now seems that some people with autism may suffer from a metabolic disorder causing them to be unable to completely digest certain foods. If

gluten (a protein found in wheat and other cereals) and casein (a protein found in cow's milk) are not properly digested, they can be broken down into peptides instead of the more usual amino acids. These peptides can mimic the many opiate-like hormones and neuro-transmitters which are involved in brain functions and may interfere with development. The child may binge on the foods which produce these opiate-like peptides, apparently craving the cause of their 'addiction' (more appropriately described as an intolerance).

Some parents are using gluten- and/or casein-free diets for their children with autistic spectrum disorders. It seems that the children most likely to benefit are those who have bowel problems such as constipation, diarrhoea or abnormal stools. Research into the effects of exclusion diets, and into the related area of using secretin, is still ongoing.

Parents can get help in planning a gluten- and/or casein-free diet from their GP, who may refer them to a dietician. Meat, vegetables and fruit will not contain gluten or casein. These are found in many processed foods, as well as in the obvious foodstuffs such as bread, biscuits and cakes (gluten), and dairy products (casein). A list of gluten-free products is available from the Coeliac Society and many supermarkets now produce lists of their products which are gluten-free. Some products are available on prescription from pharmacies; others are sold by health stores.

Sally's story

Sally Foreman – mother of Alice, aged 4 – describes her use of a gluten- and casein-free diet

"Alice has been on a gluten- and casein-free diet for 3 months now. It is working extremely well and we have seen definite improvements in several areas. The biggest improvement by far was that within a week of being on her diet, Alice started to sleep through the night. Before the diet, Alice would wake several times during the night not returning to sleep unless settled by her father or myself. On regular occasions she would wake extremely early, i.e. 2 am, and refuse to return to sleep at all. On the two occasions that Alice did sleep through the night we felt the need to check on her to ensure she was still alive! If we had a night where each of us only had to get up to her once, we felt we had had a good night.

"Since we started Alice on her diet, she is much calmer, less hyper, and has lost several bad habits. She used to grind her teeth, dig her fingers under her ribs and make a long, drawn-out "er" sound repeatedly. All of these have just about disappeared. She also seems much more alert, and responds to her name being called and simple requests much more often than before. It has been noticed that her babbling (Alice is still non-verbal) sounds much more like real words than ever before, even to the point of us waiting with baited breath, sure that a word was going to pop out any minute. Smiles, giggles and laughter were there before, but are more frequent now, giving the general impression that Alice is a much happier little girl, and eye contact has improved noticeably.

"We have had comments about how she is "coming on" from all sorts of sources and positive reports back from nursery school, stating that Alice is showing more interest in the toys and routines and even starting to follow simple routines without being prompted. We have seen good improvements in Alice since starting the diet, which easily outweigh any minor inconveniences of avoiding gluten and casein. The biggest drawback as far as Alice is concerned is that she can no longer have chocolate! As a self-confessed chocaholic I really feel for her, but it just has to be and we have found other treats she can have, though admittedly nothing quite gives the same pleasure as chocolate.

"Starting the diet was a bit daunting at first, but once into it we found it relatively easy. She can have any fruit, vegetable or fresh meat (but not processed, such as beef burgers or sausages), rice, gluten-free pasta and soya milk. The list is actually endless, but I would recommend that it is only undertaken with the help of a dietician, who can point the way to many sources of information, such as supermarkets who will provide lists of their products that are suitable. Also the co-operation of a GP is essential, as some gluten-free items are available on prescription, if the GP is willing to prescribe them. We are able to obtain gluten-free pasta, flour, biscuits, crispbread and bread this way. Without this help it would be considerably more difficult but still possible, as health food shops stock suitable products, but it would obviously be more expensive.

"Overall the effects on Alice have been very positive and I hope this will continue. If nothing else, it is worth it for the good night's sleep the whole family has now. This alone makes other problems less severe as we can cope with them much better, and Alice gets less tired, less grumpy parents into the bargain! This has got to be a good deal for everyone!"

Using computer software at home

Children on the autistic spectrum are often quick to grasp the operation of a home computer and enjoy the visual and logical nature of 'interaction' with a PC. As with video, this attraction may need to be kept under control to avoid it becoming an obsession, but can also be developed as a learning tool.

As yet, autism-specific software is in short supply, but readers of the NAS Communication magazine (Spring 1999) shared suggestions of software which their child had found attractive. Some of the packages mentioned as being suitable for the pre-school child with autism are given here.

The Springs Community

Coast Drive, St Mary's Bay,
Romney Marsh Kent TN29 0HN
Telephone: 01797 363550

The Springs Community is a spacious residential home on the Kent Coast offering high quality specialist services to adults affected by autism and Asperger's Syndrome. The main building accommodates twelve residents in single en-suite rooms. A terrace of four 'semi-independent' houses will be available in the grounds. Facilities include:-

- large television lounge; quiet lounge; fully-equipped training kitchen; private room with entertaining facilities for residents' visitors; minibuses and cars available for residents' use; menus to suit individual preferences and specialised diets

- excellent sporting and recreational facilities including fully-equipped gymnasium, full sized outdoor heated swimming pool, tennis court and squash court

- qualified and caring staff – available day and night – who support residents' individual development programmes

- large gardens with private access to beach and safe walking and cycling areas along the sea wall; shopping facilities, cafes, restaurants, community agencies etc. within walking distance; frequent bus services to surrounding towns

For an information pack or more information
please contact the manager
Registered in the Autism Services Accreditation Programme

Katherine's story

Katherine Mendham – mother of Tony, age 3½ – describes how he reacted to the introduction of a home computer

"As part of our behavioural intervention programme we were asked to find toys our autistic son found motivating. We found Tony liked best 'cause and effect' toys and in particular those small, dedicated computers for children (e.g. Vtech IQ builders). Amazed by how well Tony worked through the programmes and delighted to discover in therapy how he had learnt number, letters and spellings, we soon moved on to computer software for our PC.

"Tony is an able visual learner but with very little language so we deliberately chose software where it was necessary for Tony to listen in order to respond to the computer. We now include the computer in therapy and I buy software relevant to the subjects being taught."

The Jump Ahead Series, published by Cendant software, seems very popular and has parent support material to guide use at home. The CD ROMs cost around £20 - 25 but special offers may be available. The Jump Ahead Series is recommended as starting off in a user-friendly way and working on strength skills such as visual memory. Reader Rabbit's Toddler, from Learning Company, is also aimed at pre-school children and is recommended as easy to use, with no need to click the mouse, but introducing counting, colours, shapes and the alphabet.

Conclusion

There are various options available for pre-school intervention. The choice of which one is best will probably vary according to personal prefences, finances and time available. There is evidence that these can assist a young child in adapting to his or her surroundings and, while not providing any form of 'cure', can help improve their quality of life.

Books and resources

Visual strategies for improving communication, L. Hodgdon, 1995, Quirk Roberts Publishing. Available from Winslow Press, Telford Road, Bicester, Oxon OX6 0TS or free☎ 0800 243755.

Special diets for special kids. Understanding and implementing special diets to aid in the treatment of autism and related developmental disorders, Lisa Lewis, Future Horizons, 1999, £16.95, ISBN 1855477449 (Available from the NAS.)

Diets - www.GFCFDiet.com.

The NAS has various factsheet available.

Further information

NAS EarlyBird Programme – www.oneworld.org/autism_uk/nas/earlybi or NAS EarlyBird Centre, Manvers House, Pioneer Close, Wath-Upon-Dearne, Rotherham, South Yorkshire S63 7JZ, ☎ 01709 761 273, fax 01709 763 234, earlybird@dial.pipex.com

LOVAAS/ABA – PEACH (Parents for the Early Intervention of Autism in Children), School of Education, Brunel University, 300 St Margaret's Road, Twickenham, TW1 1PT, ☎ 0181 891 0121 x2348/2006, peach@brunel.ac.uk, www.peach.uk.com/

Option Institute's Son-Rise Program is available from Autism Treatment Center of America, THE SON-RISE PROGRAM, The Option Institute, 2080 S Undermountain Road, Sheffield, MA 01257, USA, ☎ 00 1 413 229 3202, sonrise@option.org, www.option.org/

PECS – Pyramid Educational Consultants UK Ltd, 17 Prince Albert Street, Brighton, East Sussex BN1 1HF, ☎ 01273 728888, www.pecs-uk.com/page5

Diets – Coeliac Society, PO Box 220, High Wycombe, Bucks HP11 2HY, ☎ 01494 437278, 9.30am – 2.30pm.

Exclusion diets – The Autism Research Unit, School of Health Sciences, University of Sunderland, SE2 7EE, aru@sunderland.ac.uk

Stockists of special needs software include:
REM (Rickett Educational Media), Great Weston House, Langport, Somerset TA10 9YU, ☎ 01458 253636.

SEMERC, 1 Broadbent Road, Watersheddings, Oldham OL1 4LB, ☎ 0161 827 2778, fax 0161 627 2966.

LOGOTRON, 124 Cambridge Science Park, Milton Road, Cambridge CB4 4ZS, ☎ 01223 425558.

SHERSTON, Angel House, Sherston, Malmesbury, Wiltshire SN16 0LH, ☎ 01666 840433.

Widgit Software Ltd, 102 Radford Road, Leamington Spa CV31 1LF, ☎ 01926 885303, fax 01926 885293, literacy@widgit.com, www.widgit.com.

Resources (Flying Start software), 51 High Street, Kegworth, Derby DE74 2DA, ☎ 01509 672222, fax 01509 672267, info@resourcekt.co.uk, www.resourcekt.co.uk

Education Education Education

Nell Munro, NAS Autism Helpline

Introduction

The question of what is the best type of educational provision for children with autism has been hotly debated since the condition was first recognised in the 1940s. Since then many different types of approach have been tried. Some of these are now recognised to be ineffective but many have proved helpful for at least some children. Most experts now recognise that a spectrum of provision needs to be available to provide for the spectrum of needs that exist. This fits in with the broader framework of education legislation which makes clear that children with special educational needs should receive provision which caters for them as individuals. To plan provision like this successfully it is important that schools, parents and children themselves are able to work together and can communicate effectively.

Education, however appropriate or well structured, cannot 'cure' autism. But carefully planned teaching by people who understand some of the implications of having autism can do a lot to improve children's long-term opportunities.

Partnership with parents

The 1994 Code of Practice for the Identification and Assessment of Special Educational Needs states that "Children's progress will be impaired if their parents are not seen as full and complete partners in the assessment process". This and the accompanying legislation demonstrate the commitment that is felt towards effective communication and co-operation with parents. From the parental point of view this is most likely to be seen at the time when their child's special educational needs are originally being identified and assessed, particularly if this does not occur until the child has started school.

Sadly, because there are often many different professionals involved in the assessment, statementing and monitoring processes, and because parents may not share their detailed knowledge of the education system, effective partnership with parents often seems like little more than a pipe dream. However, since 1994 central government money has been available to fund parent partnership services which either operate through the LEA or are run by local voluntary organisations. A parent partnership should be able to advise parents on all aspects of the education system and provide them with advocacy and support at reviews, assessments and tribunals. New SEN legislation will make this service statutory, so all LEAs will be expected to provide them. The NAS has lobbied long and hard for autism to be put on the agenda.

School curricula for children with autism

The National Curriculum applies to all children whether or not they have SEN. Children can be exempted if they have very severe disabilities and non-maintained schools can also opt out. The recent revisions of the National Curriculum have aimed to make it more inclusive of children with SEN and has offered guidance on adapting the curriculum for this group of pupils. This may have many benefits for pupils with autism particularly if it allows parents and teachers to work together in planning a relevant and attainable curriculum for pupils with autism.

In NAS schools, the concept of a 24-hour curriculum is emphasised. This means that every minute of the day is treated as a potential learning experience and encourages an holistic approach to learning. Many children, and not just those with autism, can benefit from this approach and this is where working with the school can be invaluable. It may be worth establishing goals in the IEP (individual education plan) which the child and their family can work on at home as well as at school. These goals could be school and education oriented, such as always completing work they are set or learning to tidy up after finishing an activity, or they could be leisure oriented, such as learning to use money or make a simple meal.

Inclusion

In recent years the move towards greater inclusion of children with SEN in the mainstream has gained momentum. Some LEAs have successfully experimented with more inclusive provision and the trend in recent legislation and guidance documents has been towards inclusion. Inclusion in the sense used by campaigners means children with SEN actively participating in the work of the mainstream class. Effective inclusion is often more expensive than placing a child in special school provision, so LEAs which are moving towards inclusive education should not be seen to be doing this to save money.

Many children with autism can learn effectively within the mainstream provided they are given appropriate support. Others are happier and more able to learn in special school provision. For some children it is desirable to have both types of provision available so that they can move between the two. Although the inclusion movement is likely to grow stronger the individual needs of the child should continue to be of paramount importance in deciding where they are placed.

This chapter uses three case studies to highlight some of the issues that are of concern primarily to parents but may also be of interest to teachers and other professionals. Although reading the case studies may give you an idea of which areas are most relevant to you, you may also find sections that are relevant and of interest in other parts of the chapter. There are also sections on further reading (this could be passed on to your child's school) and useful contacts provided at the end.

Assessment and finding a school

"I got my life back when Joe"s school was sorted out." Joe's mother

The experiences of Joe's family highlight the huge importance of LEAs finding new ways of working with families. The battle that Joe's family went through to get his SEN met was evidently a largely unnecessary strain placed on a family at a time when they had little resource left for dealing with it. Because autism tends to be diagnosed much later than other learning disabilities, there is often a very short space of time between the family learning of the child's diagnosis and their having to get involved in the

Joe's story

Joe is 7 years old and attends an NAS school where he boards during the week. Joe was diagnosed as having severe autism when he was nearly 4. He had a very successful nursery placement but his family encountered problems when it came to finding a school that was suitable for him.

The first school they visited was for pupils with moderate learning difficulties. Although in many ways it seemed like an excellent placement, his parents were worried that the school might not be able to offer Joe the level of support he needed. The LEA encouraged them to look at schools for pupils with severe learning difficulties but his parents were discouraged by the very complex needs of some of the other pupils. At this point Joe's mother got the opportunity to visit one of the NAS schools and knew straight away that this was the right place for Joe.

However, convincing the LEA of this was still a battle. They refused to fund a place for Joe at the NAS school because they had decided to open their own autism unit attached to a special school. Joe's parents were still convinced that they had found him the right placement and continued to fight for this. Eventually after much pressure and after a local councillor had intervened on their behalf, the LEA relented and Joe started at Radlett Lodge the following term.

statementing process and identifying the school they want their child to attend. This means that at the point where families may have to fight the LEA for a placement they are also at their most stressed and vulnerable.

For parents it is often helpful to talk things through with other people who have been in a similar position. This is where local support groups can be valuable (contact the Autism Helpline for more information). Parents can also try calling the Parent to Parent Helpline (details at the end of the chapter).

Many, but not all, children with autism will have a statement of SEN drawn up by their LEA. This document should contain a description of the child's difficulties and specify the kind of provision they need. If the statement is being drawn up before the child starts school, parents will need to choose which school they want their child to attend. Choosing a school is not easy, and choosing a special school may be even harder because there are fewer schools available.

These are just some general tips for looking at schools:

- Try and see as many different types of school as you can and don't be discouraged by other people's comments. Joe's mother was initially discouraged from seeing Radlett Lodge because of comments made by his speech and language therapist. It was only by going to see it herself that she was able to decide it was the right place for him.
- With autism, nothing is set in stone. Your child might benefit more from a placement in a school for children with moderate learning difficulties than from an autism specific unit. Your child's individual need and not the definition of a school's intake should determine where they are placed.
- Before visiting a school try and draw up a list of the areas in which your child demonstrates their greatest strengths and weaknesses. Try and keep this list in mind when you visit. The right school should be able to encourage your child's strengths and help them develop in their areas where they have most difficulty.
- Bear in mind that schools can be adaptable too. Schools which initially seem unsuitable may be able to do little things like allow your child to miss the end of assemblies or not play competitive sports if you feel that they wouldn't be able to cope with this.
- Don't feel ashamed to ask as many questions as you want. If you come away from your visit with more questions to ask it is fine to call the school or write to them for more information.

"When Joe started at Radlett I felt I no longer had to worry about the 'cure' thing. I felt able to accept that Joe had autism and was going to be an adult with autism as well." Joe's mother

Working with the school

Joe's school works closely with his family to ensure that they are kept fully informed about everything he is doing. The fact that the parents and school established a good working relationship early on has clearly made this easier.

Portfield School

4 Magdalen Lane
Christchurch
Dorset
BH23 1PH

Tel: 01202 486626
Fax: 01202 483677
E-mail portfield@lds.co.uk

Portfield school is a day and weekly residential school for children with autism aged 2 - 19. The main aims of our school education are to help the children overcome and cope with the triad of impariments, and to maximise their opportunities for independent living.

The school:

- has recently enjoyed favourable OFSTED and social services inspections.

- is committed to high quality training for all of its staff.

- employs its own specialist speech and language therapist, music therapist and educational psychologist.

- has successfuly gained planning premission to build new purpose build premises in order to expand provision for 63 pupils

- is committed to the use of non-aversive and positive methods of behavioural intervention.

- is involved in many succesful integration projects and liaises closely with local mainstream schools

- is registered and fully accredited as part of the National Autistic Society quality audit and accrediation programme.

If you would like further details please contact Peter Gabony, the Head teacher, in order to receive our brochure or arrange a visit.

"When the head said 'We'd be delighted to have him' I felt it was the first time someone had positively wanted Joe." Joe's mother

However, it is crucial that this good communication continues and that as many lines of communication between the school and home are kept open as possible. Young people with autism benefit from receiving consistent messages about their behaviour and this is only achievable if schools and families are able to work together. Lines of communication can include:

- Homework diaries or communication books.
- Meeting with teachers informally, for example when you are picking your child up from school.
- Meeting with teachers formally. If your child has a statement then you should be able to discuss concerns with the school at the annual review, but they should also arrange parents evenings more frequently.
- Annual reports and statement reviews. These should inform you not only of your child's academic progress but also of how they are coping with all aspects of school life.

Education

James' story

James is 15 years old and has Asperger syndrome. He spent most of his primary education at a mainstream school and then moved to a school for children with complex or medical needs. Recently he moved to a school for children with autism where he is doing really well.

The main reason for the move was that James was very unhappy at his old school. The teachers and other pupils found it hard to understand which areas James had difficulties in. James was often very anxious because he wasn't sure what was expected of him. His anxiety was more apparent at home than at school where James appeared to be studious but withdrawn.

The success of the move can be seen in his willingness to talk about the new school. Although the change in environment has taken a bit of getting used to, James is clearly much calmer and happier now. And this in turn is making it easier for him to learn and develop new skills.

At school

Attitudes and expectations

"At my old school some of the teachers were horrible. Now they are relaxed and cheerful." James

As James puts it, the attitudes of teachers can make all the difference to a child with autism. Children and young people with autism are very able to pick up on the attitudes and expectations of those around them. However, they may have problems interpreting these. An eagerness to say what they think the teacher wants to hear rather than what they truly think can have very negative repercussions. It is important for children with autism to be clear about the expectations of those around them.

If this is to be effective then it is crucial that the school and family are able to communicate. James was in the confusing position of being perceived as an extremely good pupil even though he was often struggling to cope at school. It would have been helpful if the school had made more of an effort to find out about how James was coping outside school hours. Young people with high-functioning autism or Asperger syndrome can be particularly good at bottling up their feelings and only releasing them in an environment in which they feel safe. It is a strange paradox, but if a young person with Asperger syndrome does become agitated or angry at school on occasion it may indicate that in the main they feel relatively secure there. It was James' long-term insecurities that were preventing him from expressing his feelings.

Breaks

Unstructured breaks can be a nightmare for children with autism. Playground culture can make them vulnerable to bullying and if midday assistants do not understand their needs then they may be very poorly protected. A playground can be a very frightening place for a young person with autism. The high levels of stimulation available can be unbearably distracting and in turn cause great anxiety.

However, all young people need time out and children with autism also need the opportunity to learn how to cope with unstructured time. What works for James is having plenty of short breaks between lessons. A common room is available where there aren't likely to be many other students. Rather than unlimited choices, which can too easily become no choice at all, James is able to choose between a few activities which suit him. Because break time is dispersed across the day, only a few students are out at any one time. This works well in a special school setting, but in the mainstream there are clear practical barriers which might prevent this happening.

Teachers could, however, try:

- Talking with the student and their family to establish at what times they might need time out.
- Work with learning support assistants and the young person to find a way for them to effectively communicate when they need a break.

Ways of giving time out during lessons could include:

- Giving the young person a note to take to the school office. The note could just ask whoever receives it to thank the young person and send them back to their lesson. The few minutes outside the classroom may be all it takes for the young person to calm down.
- Structuring all lessons so that any period of small group work (this is likely to be the period a young person with autism finds most stressful) is followed by some individual study.

The Autism Service Accreditation Programme
Promoting Quality Services for
Children and Adults with Autism

The Autism Services Accreditation Programme is owned by the NAS but operates as an independent services to ensure consistent standards are achieved whether the care services is provided by the NAS, a local society, a local authority or another independent organisation.

The Programme, the only one of its kind in the world as far as we are aware, provides an autism specific benchmark of quality. Its aim is to assist, support and encourage all services for people with autistic spectrum disorders to attain and retain accreditation. This ensures that a service meets national standards and responds effectively and appropriately to the special needs of people with autism, both children and adults. At present there are over 100 separate services registered with the programme. For details of these services see Section VII - Useful contacts.

Any service provider who is committed to the development of specialised high quality services for children and adults with autism can participate in this programme which leads to the service being accredited. This includes specialist agencies and those in the voluntary, private and public sectors including education, health and social services.

For further information, please contact
The Autism Services Accreditation Programme
236 Henleaze Road, Bristol BS9 4NG
Telephone: 0117 962 8962   Fax: 0117 962 2220
Email: ACCPROG@dial.pipex.com

During structured breaks such as the lunch hour, a midday assistant or learning support assistant could be asked to spend some time with them each day working on joining groups or playing with others. This need be no more than 10-15 minutes but it can serve a valuable double purpose. Besides giving the young person the opportunity and support they need to work with others, it may also signify to other children in the playground that the young person is being protected and is not a good target for bullying.

Safety and perceived safety

"I can trust people." James

It is naturally very difficult to learn in an environment in which you do not feel safe. For James, anxiety was beginning to define his education. Parents and professionals working with children with autism have a big problem to contend with here. It is easy to see that a child who is vulnerable to playground bullying will not feel safe but it is often harder to understand the many other issues that can contribute to a young person's anxiety levels.

Children with autism have great difficulty imagining alternative outcomes. As a result, seemingly small problems can grow out of all proportion. One child described being worried that their pen might run out. It did not occur to them that if this happened they could simply ask for another one. Instead, they tried writing as small as they possibly could in order to preserve the ink they had left. Naturally, this eventuality could not be anticipated but schools and parents can still consider the number of ways in which children with autism can be made to feel more safe.

"It's good to be able to tell people if something is too difficult or too easy." James

The key to this is communication. Communicating a consistent message to the young person that it is OK to talk is vital. James was fortunate in that he had friends and family outside his school who were able to understand his feelings. Some young people may not be in this position, and even those who are can still be inhibited from discussing their real fears and anxieties. Fears cannot be allayed by words alone and it needs to be evident to the young person that what they say will not be treated harshly or, worse, ignored.

"The other pupils are quiet too. At my old school they were too noisy." James

Many small factors may contribute to a young person's unwillingness to communicate their needs. Among these could be the behaviour of other pupils or the way classes are organised or structured. It is helpful if teachers can ensure that time is available for young people to feed back their concerns. This could happen during one-to-one sessions in class, after a class or could be arranged as a formal consultation during the lunch hour or after school. Where other pupils might be able to raise their hand and say they like the blinds down, this could be near impossible for the student with autism. So it is vital that teachers are that bit extra vigilant.

Bullying

"For me it matters that he enjoys his education, I'm more worried about that than his exam results." Samuel's father

Bullying is common. Virtually all young people are likely to be affected by it either directly or indirectly during their education. However, this does not in anyway make it acceptable and most mainstream and special schools now accept that it is a problem which should be dealt with actively.

All schools should have an anti-bullying policy which parents are entitled to see. Many will also have appointed a teacher with specific responsibility for co-ordinating and monitoring the anti-bullying policy. If your child is starting at a mainstream school it might be helpful to meet with this teacher to discuss your concerns.

Young people with autism may be particularly at risk of bullying because their behaviour can stand out and make them easy targets. When starting secondary school they will be joining a group of other young people who are all trying desperately hard to define and assert their own identities. Adolescents can be prone to unintentionally bullying and victimising others. They may pick on the child with autism not out of animosity but simply because they feel vulnerable and insecure themselves. However, the secondary school may have some advantages over primary school.

Samuel's story

Samuel is 12 years old and has Asperger syndrome. He attended a mainstream primary school where he coped well. His parents were keen for him to be able to attend a mainstream secondary school as well. Choosing a suitable school was not easy, but they eventually picked a grammar school with an excellent academic record.

Samuel was the first pupil they had ever taken with a statement of special educational needs, and the school were anxious to do their best for him. Before he started all staff attended a talk given by an expert on Asperger syndrome who knew Samuel. They also worked with his parents to find out what things were worrying them.

Samuel has now been at the school for a year and seems to be enjoying it. There have been a few minor problems but many of these have been ironed out through collaboration between the school, his parents and most importantly Samuel himself.

Education

"It's good that there are things to do in break-times like library and computer club. At my old school we all had to go in the playground". Samuel

Indications that your child is being bullied might range from the very obvious, such as injuries or a strong reluctance to go to school, to the subtle, such as an avoidance of certain lessons or a willingness to talk about their lessons but not about other pupils. Young people with autism may not have the language skills that will allow them to explain they are being bullied. Find out what your child understands by the term 'bullied'. They may take it very literally as being beaten up in the playground and not realise that the name-calling or the fact that some people always avoid them is also a form of bullying. They may also find it very hard to describe how this makes them feel. Drawing up a simple concrete definition of bullying with your child can be a really good way of empowering them.

WARGRAVE HOUSE SCHOOL
449 Wargrave Road
Newton-le-Willows
Merseyside, WA12 8RS

Principal: Mrs Pam Maddock B.Ed. (Hons) DIP. T.O.M.H.

Tel: 01925 224899   Fax: 01925 291368

"This is a very good school with many outstanding features"

"The ethos of the school is excellent"
(OFSTED Report)

Wargrave House is a day and weekly boarding independent school with a population of 62 mixed ability pupils who have autistic spectrum disorder. The school has a Further Education Unit for students between the ages of 16 and 19. The catchment area is the North West of England.

The school's ethos is centred around the belief in strong partnership with parents/carers and shared aims and practical cooperation draws on this breadth of intimate knowledge and expertise.

We incorporate a functional and pragmatic approach to learning which is concerned with both the process and the product of education

An example of a definition could be:

- A bully is someone who deliberately tries to make you feel bad.
- They can do this by calling you names you don't like, by ignoring you or by avoiding you, by beating you up or trying to start fights with you. All of these things could be bullying.
- Sometimes just one person might be doing the bullying, sometimes it might be a group of people.
- It is very hard to tackle a bully by yourself. You should ask for help. You can ask your parents or your teacher for help.

It is important to emphasise to the school that while your child may appear to understand this they may still have difficulty applying it to their own experiences. They may need to be reminded of it frequently (for example, you can write this down on cue cards which could be stuck in their homework diary as a way of reminding them) and teachers will still need to watch out for signs of bullying.

In Samuel's case bullying has not been too much of a problem. Where he has been teased or picked on he has had the confidence to speak directly to his head of year who has then acted straight away.

Teachers could also bear in mind the following points.

Bully and stress free: a child enjoying school.

Don't:

- Ignore the problem just because the pupil or their parents aren't complaining.
- Assume the pupil is asking for it. They may not understand why their behaviour makes them a target for bullies.

And do:

- Remember that pupils with autism may be perpetrators as well as victims. If they are bullying other pupils again, they may not realise what impact their behaviour is having. And they may be doing it as a way of protecting themselves. There are a number of strategies which teachers can employ to help reduce the risk of bullying. If the young person is willing to explain their autism to the class then this may make it easier for other pupils to empathise with them and understand why they may behave differently. If this is a success then you can also introduce the idea of building up a circle of friends. A circle of friends is a group of students who volunteer to befriend the pupil with autism. They can provide positive input on developing social skills and also give the young person some protection from bullies particularly during lunch hours and break times.

Coping with schoolwork, homework and time management

The problems a child with autism will experience with schoolwork may be hard to predict. Even where a child or young person with autism is highly intelligent they can still have difficulties managing their work which belies their actual ability.

Presentation

"Presentation was a problem...Sam didn't understand why neatness mattered to other people if he knew what he was writing about." Samuel's father

In Samuel's case the difficulties he had with presenting his work neatly were not anticipated by his school or family. Samuel's problems with presentation were a result of his not being able to understand how other people think. It was very hard for him to see that the person marking his work would need to understand it as well as him. It was getting a bad report which criticised his presentation, even though he had a good understanding, which brought home to him that he needed to make himself clearer. Clear explanations of the links between a clear understanding, producing good work and receiving good marks can be very helpful.

Products and processes

Children and young people generally tend to have a preoccupation with products or the end result of what they are doing rather than the process of learning. In children with autism this bias can be very strongly towards one type of learning or the other. For example, some young people with autism may feel they haven't achieved anything if the kite they are making in an art or craft lesson fails to fly. Others might have no interest in end products and produce a series of half finished projects for which they get very low marks. It is important to explain this to your child's school and to identify in which area they have most difficulty. By doing so you can start positively rewarding them in the area where they show least motivation. The child who has to get things done could be praised for their team work skills wherever possible, and the child who is not motivated to complete anything could be given extra support to get at least one thing done and then be rewarded with good marks and positive reinforcement.

Sequencing

'I just learnt my timetable by heart straightaway...sometimes I still forgot what to take though'. Samuel

People with autism often experience difficulty with social cueing and sequencing. This can make understanding why and when things happen very difficult.

For example, it was hard for Samuel to link up the concept of a PE lesson at 2pm meaning that he had to change and take his PE kit to change into. One way of dealing with problems like this is to make a visual timetable for the young person. A visual timetable uses symbols and photographs as well as words to remind the young person of the content of their lessons as well as what they are called. It might also help to incorporate what types of equipment are needed for each lesson into the body of the timetable. Working with the young person to draw this up will help to ensure that it is relevant to them.

Social stories

An excellent approach to helping a young person understand these problems is using 'social stories'. A social story is short story written in a special style or format that describes social situations in terms of relevant social cues and

The **Scottish Society** for **Autism**

Clannalba Respite Centre

Clannalba Respite Centre, the base for the Society's Respite Care and Family Support Services, sits in its own pleasant grounds surrounded by beautiful countryside in the small hamlet of Lamington, near Biggar, in South Lanarkshire.

The facilities have been extended with the addition of a purpose built multi-sensory stimulation room and therapy pool, and an outdoor play area.

HOW TO ACCESS SERVICES

Clients will normally be referred through, and funded by, statutory services (Social Work, Health, Education). The Society is, however, able to advise parents/carers on procedures to obtain a referral.

For further information, a referral form, or to arrange a meeting to discuss a client's needs, please contact:

Centre Manager
The Scottish Society for Autism
Clannalba Respite Centre,
Lamington, Biggar ML12 6HP

Tel: (01899) 850633
Fax: (01899) 850330

For further information on other autism-specific services, contact:
The Scottish Society for Autism
(formerly The Scottish Society for Autistic Children)
Head Office: Hilton House, Alloa Business Park,
Whins Road, Alloa FK10 3SA
Email: autism@autism-in-scotland.org.uk
Website: www.autism-in-scotland.org.uk
Tel: (01259) 720044   Fax: (01259) 720051
Scottish Charity No: SC 009068

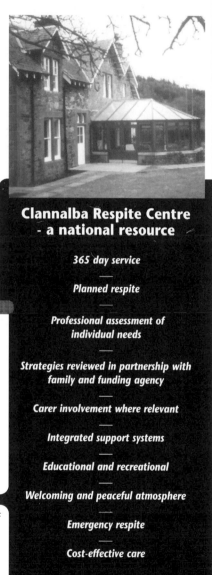

Clannalba Respite Centre - a national resource

365 day service

Planned respite

Professional assessment of individual needs

Strategies reviewed in partnership with family and funding agency

Carer involvement where relevant

Integrated support systems

Educational and recreational

Welcoming and peaceful atmosphere

Emergency respite

Cost-effective care

common responses. The approach was devised by an American expert on education and autism called Carol Gray and one of the books at the end of this chapter gives more details of how to devise social stories.

Another strategy that may help involves giving the young person cue cards to take with them through the day. If they have particular difficulty with generalising their experiences, then it can be extremely helpful to have a card in their homework diary or attached to their exercise book saying "You can ask a teacher for help whenever you need to" or "If you feel anxious you can ask to take a quick break to calm down".

Homework

Homework may be a new problem when the child starts secondary school, as they may not have experienced this before or if they have it may have been quite informal. Before your child changes schools it might be helpful to introduce the idea of homework to them and talk about how they will have to spend some time working each evening. Think about how you can fit homework into their current routine. Is it better for them to do their homework before or after dinner? Where should they to do their homework? How can we minimise distractions? Make sure your child is clear about why they are doing homework. Explain that it is to help them understand things better at school and is a means to an end, not an end in itself.

Teaching your child time-management skills can be very difficult and is something you could collaborate on with the school. Children with autism often learn to tell the time very quickly and it may appear that their understanding of this is very good. However, their understanding is often very literal and tied up with concepts of clocks and watches. Most people actually understand time in terms of what can be achieved within a certain period. For example, to most of us 10 mins is the time it takes to walk half a mile, but to a child with autism it is the time it takes for the long hand to move between the 12 and the two.

Providing a very precise timetable is one way of ensuring that your child can cope with time management during the school day, but outside school you may need to work on broadening their understanding. You can try suggesting how long things take in relation to other activities. Instead of saying "Do your homework for half an hour and watch TV afterwards" you could suggest ""Watch Eastenders and then work for the same amount of time on your homework". You can ask your child's school to emphasise this message as well.

Transition and further education for students

The transition from child to adult services and from compulsory to further and higher education can be difficult for all young people. For young people with autism these difficulties are compounded by their problems with adapting to change and understanding alternative outcomes. However, the transition may also be very positive and open up many new opportunities. In order for this process to be successful the transition needs to be clearly planned and have the full involvement of all the people involved in your child's life.

Choosing a college

There are a wide variety of different placements available for students with autism. You might want your son or daughter to continue in their current provision until they are 18 or 19. In the main, LEAs are happy to fund special school placements until 19. However, your child may be at a school which has no post 16 provision, in which case you will need to look at the range of provision available locally. When visiting mainstream colleges, even if your child will be attending a specialist unit within the college, it is important to look out for:

- Meeting with staff. Do they seem to understand what autism is? If they don't would they be prepared to do some training and learn more?

Glasgow Nautical College

Glasgow Nautical College were approached by the Strathclyde Autistic Society who were concerned at the lack of provision locally for students with Asperger syndrome post 16. They worked with the Society as well as with representatives from the NAS and, most importantly, parents to design a program called 'Transition', specifically for this group of young people. The course is designed to equip students with the skills they will need to either find employment or progress to other further education courses.

Key elements of the Transition programme are:

- Peer mentoring – the opportunity for all students on the course to work with other students at the college on different courses. This promotes the integration of the students and also allows them to see what other opportunities are available to them once they finish the course.
- A mixture of classes covering both academic skills and independent living skills. Although the main emphasis of the course is on the development of practical life skills, there is also the opportunity for students to continue to study subjects which are of interest to them. This is important as it allows for continuity between school and college.
- A 'named person' will be available to students at all times so that they can feed back their concerns and receive one to one support and guidance.

It is intended for the course programme to be made available to other FE colleges free of charge, so that more students will have the opportunity to benefit from it.

Although this course is only available in Glasgow at present it is possible to replicate elements of it in any further education setting. For example, all students with Asperger syndrome and autism should be made aware of who they can approach when they have a problem, a structure should be in place that will make someone else available if their usual 'named person' is not.

Education

- Atmosphere and environment. Is the college very big? Can it be quite noisy? Are the corridors crowded? Are there any calm places where your child can take a break for 10 mins?
- Socialising. Does the college organise social activities or are students supposed to take most of the responsibility for making links on themselves? Will your child be moving on there with other people they have known at school or will everyone be new?
- How much responsibility are students meant to take for their own learning? How much study support is provided? Is you child ready to cope with this? Some children with high functioning autism may be able to take 'A' levels but still choose to take a vocational qualification instead as it is more structured. Taking a vocational qualification such as an NVQ or a GNVQ does not preclude the possibility of moving on to take 'A' levels afterwards.

Onwards and upwards

When choosing further education provision and courses it is important to also look at what your child is hoping to do in the long-term. They may be in a position to hold down a job, they may need to develop the skills to live semi-independently, they may need to develop the people skills that could enable them to live in supported housing with other people at some point. Working with your child to make decisions at this point is vitally important. Some ways in which you could involve them in the decision making include:

- Take them with you to visit colleges and other types of provision.
- Ask the professional advisers involved to give your child a brief resume of their role either in person or on paper so that your son or daughter can understand why they are attending meetings.
- Ask the people whom your child trusts to discuss the issues with them. Sometimes it can be easier to accept advice if it comes from someone their own age than if it is coming from a parent.
- It may be possible for your child to discuss their ambitions and aspirations more openly with someone their own age.
- Don't be afraid of conflict occurring. Learning to compromise is a vital skill for adult life. Remember that you ask your son or daughter to get involved so that they feel a degree of ownership over the decisions made. This does not mean that they should make the decisions exclusively.

Remember that while your child may have different views to you, they may be better than your own, so keep an open mind.

Conclusion

None of these issues are straightforward and this article is limited by the range of subjects which it attempts to cover. However, if it has a basic message it is that effective communications between schools, parents and young people are vitally important in providing children with autism with a high quality education. We often talk to people with autism of the need to meet others half way. A person with autism may need to develop some of the skills necessary to interact with those around them but equally other people should make an effort to understand their needs. This could also be applied to the relationships that exist between professionals and parents.

There are likely to be many subtle but significant changes to the legislation affecting children with SEN over the next few years. These will further emphasise the need for working together and focusing on the individual needs of the child. At the same time awareness of autism and its implications is growing among education professionals.

Books

T. Attwood, *Asperger syndrome: a guide for parents and professionals*, Jessica Kingsley, 1998, £12.95, ISBN 1853025771. This is an extremely readable introduction to Asperger syndrome, equally accessible to both parents and teachers. It provides an excellent overview of the range of areas in which a child with Asperger Syndrome may have difficulties. (Available from the NAS.)

A. Fullerton *et al., Higher functioning adolescents and young adults with autism: a teacher's guide*, Pro Ed, 1996, ISBN 0890796815. This book contains valuable sections on organisational and social skills which might be valuable for both teachers and parents. It also contains an article by Carol Gray which describes a variety of ways of helping young people with autism develop social skills.

P. Howlin *et al., Teaching children with autism to mind read: a practical guide*, John Wiley and Sons, 1998, £16.99, ISBN 04721976237. This book provides detailed information on approaches which teachers can use to improve understanding of emotions, pretence and beliefs in children with autism. (Available from the NAS.)

W. Lawson, *Life behind glass*, Southern Cross University Press, 1998, £9.99, ISBN 1875855319. The sections describing the authors school life give valuable insights into the experiences of children with autistic spectrum disorders in the mainstream.

Leicester City Council and Leicestershire County Council, *Asperger syndrome – practical strategies for the classroom: a teacher's guide*, The National Autistic Society, 1998, £8.99, ISBN 0899280014. This book was drawn up by people employed by a local education authority and is a valuable source of ideas particularly for teachers in mainstream schools.

S. Powell and R. Jordan (editors), *Autism and learning: a guide to good practice*, David Fulton Publishers, 1997, £14.00, ISBN 185346421X. This book is valuable for all teachers involved in curriculum planning for children with autism. It examines the implications of having autism on learning in specific subject areas.

D. Seach, *Autistic spectrum disorder: positive approaches for teaching children with ASD*, NASEN, 1998, ISBN 1901485013. This book is aimed primarily at teachers and offers advice on adapting the National Curriculum to meet their needs. (Available from the NAS.)

Helplines

NAS Autism Helpline ☎ 0870 600 85 85

Open between 10am and 4pm, Monday to Friday, for parents and carers. Run by the NAS, it offers advice and support on all aspects of autism and Asperger syndrome, including education.

NAS Parent to Parent ☎ 0800 9 520 520

This is a listening service staffed by parent volunteers and run by the NAS. Parents can ring the freephone number and leave a message which is picked up by a parent volunteer in their area who then returns the call.

ACE (Advisory Centre for Education) ☎ 020 7354 8321 (General),
☎ 020 7704 9822 (Exclusions)

Open between 2 and 5pm, Monday to Friday. This is a helpline for all parents and professionals, offering information, advice and referrals on a wide range of education issues. The exclusions helpline runs 2-4pm, Monday, Wednesday and Friday.

AFASIC (Association For All Speech Impaired Children) ☎ 0845 355 5577

Open between 10am and 2pm, Tuesday and Wednesday, and 10am and 12pm on Thursday. Offers advice to parents of children and young people who have a speech and/or language difficulty.

IPSEA (Independent Panel for Special Education Advisors) ☎ 0800 0184016

This helpline is staffed by professionals and offers advice on all areas of special education.

Network 81 ☎ 01279 647415

Open between 10am and 2pm, Monday to Friday. Offers advice on all matters relating to SEN. Issues dealt with include selecting a school, assessment and statementing.

autism

Published in association with
The National Autistic Society

The International Journal of Research and Practice

The launch of *Autism* reflects the recent worldwide growth in the research and understanding of autistic spectrum disorders, and the consequent impact on the provision of treatment and care.

A Major International Forum

Autism provides a major international forum for research of direct and practical relevance to improving the quality of life for individuals with autism or autism-related disorders.

Recent Contents Have Included:

◆ Neuropsychological profiles of children with Asperger syndrome and autism
  Janine Majiviona and Margot Prior

◆ Pragmatic language impairment without autism: the children in question
  Nicola Botting and Gina Conti-Ramsden

◆ Contrasting styles of drawing in gifted individuals with autism
  Maureen Cox and Kate Eames

◆ The outcome of a supported employment scheme for high functioning adults with autism or Asperger syndrome **Patricia Howlin and Lynn Mawhood**

◆ Adolescents with Asperger syndrome: three case studies of individual and family therapy
  Kevin Stoddart

◆ The experience of parents in the diagnosis of autism: a pilot study
  Kenny Midence and Meena O'Neill

Quarterly: March, June, September, December • ISSN: 1362-3613

Raising the stakes - getting funds

Lorraine Pearson

Introduction

What is fundraising all about? How can I get involved? Have I got enough time? How do I get help? The Fundraising Department at the NAS has the experience and the contacts to provide the answers to many of your questions. Fundraising is about more than raising money, it is about team effort, and it's up to you how much time you give and how you give it.

"It's does take up a lot of my spare time, but the rewards are enormous, it's enabled me to widen my circle of friends and to meet like minded parents, many of whom have experienced similar problems to ours." Sally, Brighton

"When I think of fundraising, I remember the days spent hiding from the rain and then counting money on a sodden school field after a summer downpour." Sue, London

"Rattling tins outside the local superstore, wearing an oversized yellow and black fluffy bug and feeling hot and exhausted" Joan, Cranleigh

These are just a few of the comments from new and active fundraisers in branches around the country. All of them are unanimous in the view that it has been hard work, and at times frustrating. However, accomplishing something positive has been the key for all of them.

What does the NAS do?

Fundraising is a crucial and necessary part of the work of the NAS. The NAS relies on funds from voluntary sources to support its many services. Every

Funding

JESSICA KINGSLEY PUBLISHERS

116 Pentonville Road, London, N1 9JB, UK
Tel: +44 (0)20 7833 2307 Fax: +44 (0)20 7837 2917
email: post@jkp.com website: www.jkp.com

Our list of titles on autism and Asperger's Syndrome is now amongst the foremost in the world and our books are published for people with autism and Asperger's Syndrome themselves as well as for their families, carers, and the people that work with them. We place a strong emphasis on the voice of the individual.

★ *Over 70 000 copies sold worldwide*

Asperger's Syndrome

A Guide for Parents and Professionals
Tony Attwood
Foreword by Lorna Wing
1998 240 pages ISBN 1 85302 577 1 pb £12.95

'Tony Attwood's empathy, knowledge and common-sense approach to describing individuals with Asperger's syndrome, highlighting the problems that they and their families, teachers and carers often face, and outlining the practical and achievable strategies for intervention and education is spot-on. Attwood has achieved the rare feat of describing the current state of scientific knowledge in accessible and understandable language. Everyone who works in the field, every parent, and I suspect many individuals with Asperger's syndrome will want to read this book.'
– *Clinical Child Psychology and Psychiatry*

Tony Attwood is a practising clinical psychologist who specialises in the field of Asperger's Syndrome. For the last twenty-five years he has met and worked with several hundred individuals with this syndrome, ranging widely in age, ability and background.

Parents' Education as Autism Therapists

Applied Behaviour Analysis in Context
Edited by Mickey Keenan, Ken P. Kerr
and Karola Dillenburger
Foreword by Bobby Newman
1999 240 pages ISBN 1 85302 778 2 pb £13.95

Clear, focused, and practical, this book is a useful introduction to ABA for parents and professionals working with children with autism.

In Northern Ireland the PEAT group offers parents the education necessary to become their own child's therapists using ABA. In this book these parents and the professionals involved in their training share their knowledge, experience, and successes.

Mickey Keenan is Director of PEAT and a lecturer in the Psychology Department at the University of Ulster at Coleraine; **Ken P. Kerr** is Director of Training of PEAT and a Learning and Behavioural Consultant in private practice; and **Karola Dillenburger** is a lecturer in the School of Social Work at The Queen's University of Belfast.

Pretending to be Normal

Living with Asperger's Syndrome
Liane Holliday Willey
Foreword by Tony Attwood
1999 176pp ISBN 1 85302 749 9 pb £12.95

'This book provides a wealth of information and insight into the world of the person with Asperger's Syndrome... Her experiences are reported with such clarity and detail that it becomes possible to see the world from her perspective. It offers hope and encouragement to all people with AS. Parents in particular will find this book (as I have) a comfort and a guide to a deeper understanding of the triad of impairments so characteristic of people with ASD. This book is a must for all who have the privilege of knowing someone who is an "Aspie".'
– *Centre For Social Policy Research and Development – University Of Wales, Bangor*

Liane Holliday Willey is a doctor of education, a writer and a researcher who specialises in the fields of psycholinguistics and learning style differences. Dr Willey has a wonderful husband, three happy children, dedicated parents and an active social life. She also has Asperger's Syndrome, just like her youngest daughter.

Autism and Play

Jannik Beyer and Lone Gammeltoft
1999 112pp ISBN 1 85302 845 2 pb £12.95

'This book is particularly valuable and special in that the authors provide professionals and parents with specific and precise ideas for the planning of play activities – ideas that can be applied directly. In addition, the excellent photographs supplement the educational strategies. The interesting point in this respect is that the authors describe how even very low-functioning children with autism can also benefit from play activities. This book is essential reading and a valuable source of inspiration for professionals and parents who are looking for creative and good ideas for play activities for children with autism.'
– *from the Preface by Dr Demetrious Haracopos, Director: The Danish Information and Training Center for Autism*

Jannik Beyer, PhD is a psychologist and Director of broendagerskolen, a special school for autistic children. **Lone Gammeltoft** is a speech and language therapist and teacher at the broendagerskolen.

year it seeks corporate support from industry, applies for National Lottery grants, requests support from Charitable Trusts and applies for Government funding to develop additional services. Fundraising also helps to build awareness as well as persuading health authorities, education authorities, social services and the general public that their support and commitment does make a difference.

The NAS organises major events and initiatives such as celebrity balls, sporting events, national raffles and appeals. The NAS Fundraising Department is active in campaigning via direct marketing and advertising methods to seek support. Legacy income, although largely unpredictable, plays an increasingly important part in funding work.

It is important to be aware of what is happening nationally, but the real support is needed at grass roots level – in the community. However, there is scope to generate your own ideas at local branch level, or in some instances to support the NAS through activities such as participating in the London Marathon. The NAS Fundraising Department can provide all the help and advice you need to get started, as well as supplying a list of fundraising ideas and sponsorship forms for your event. ☎ 020 7903 3522 for further information.

Where do I fit in?

Local groups benefit enormously from the time, goodwill and support given by members. The approach to raising funds is a team effort, although individual contributions are of enormous value. Once you are clearly focused on a specific project, you will need to know how to go about setting up a fundraising committee and what method you should use to solicit a good response. It's important to have a clear, well thought out strategy.

Setting up an event from scratch need not be difficult. It could be something as simple as swimming 50 lengths of the local swimming pool, taking a 10 mile hike or organising a sweepstake. Often the simplest ideas are the most effective.

No matter how little time you have to offer, you can make a valuable contribution to the team effort. If you have very little spare time, consider

Funding

options that require little organisation. Maybe you have a professional skill that could prove useful to your local branch, like designing or printing posters or tickets, writing a newsletter, talking to the local media or offering a service, such as personal training or beauty treatments, that might make excellent prizes in a raffle or auction. Write to members of your branch, telling them about your ideas for raising funds and requesting volunteers for a fundraising committee. Allocate specific tasks to committee members and hold regular meetings to get a progress report. Contact other support groups in the area, local colleges, schools, youth groups or other voluntary groups who might also be interested in getting involved.

Ideas for getting started

You can contribute to local branch funds in the simplest of ways. Keep a collection box at home to collect loose change, or introduce a swear box. If you give up something like smoking, save the money instead, or if you are feeling really brave, volunteer to have your beard or head shaved. If you're sporty, organise your favourite team sports and raise money by charging a small entrance fee. Ask another organisations like the local Rotary club or scouts if they might hold a fundraising event on your behalf.

Ask the children to sort out unwanted toys and give the whole family a chance to have a clear out. You'll find lots of items to sell in a garage or car boot sale. Find out about local fetes and fairs and arrange to have a stall there to raise funds, or suggest that a local school have a non-uniform day with all the pupils making a small donation. Encourage the children to do odd jobs for a fee, organise a street collection or sell NAS lapel badges.

Raffles are simple to organise and effective but are governed by certain rules that can mean a licence may be required. If you need advice on raffles, contact the NAS Fundraising Department for more information on the rules and regulations.

A street collection permit is required for those carrying collection tins in the street, and some councils don't permit collections in the park. If applying for a permit, do so as far ahead as possible (there are often restrictions on Saturdays). If you cannot obtain one, you may be able to get permission from a local shopping centre, motorway service station, railway station, supermarket or concert venue. Don't collect money from the public without permission from the landowners and never use a bucket – it's illegal. Collecting door-to-door or in pubs also requires a house-to-house collecting licence and all collectors must be over 16. Contact the NAS Fundraising Department for official NAS collecting tins with security seals and an identification sticker.

It should not be necessary to spend money to get prizes. Ask local shops and businesses to donate items in exchange for some publicity at the event or on the tickets. Plan to contact them in plenty of time before the event.

How to get funding

If you feel that your event has a good chance of attracting a lot of people and publicity you may want to look for funding. Consider approaching local businesses well in advance, with a view to securing sponsorship. Present them with a professional looking, detailed proposal about the event, including estimated attendance, publicity and advertising plans, and the opportunities for the company name to be displayed in association with the event, for example on promotional banners or T-shirts.

Some venues and businesses offer special reduced rates for fundraising events and some may be persuaded to offer their services for free. You could also find out about your employer's policy on employee fundraising. Many companies will match the amount raised by their employee while others prefer to donate a straight sum.

A government grant can provide major funding, but this is often difficult to obtain and time consuming, and the NAS Fundraising Department handles these bids. There are, however, a number of small grant programmes on offer; full details are available from the National Council for Voluntary Organisations. Local authorities are responsible for areas which cover education, social services, recreation and leisure services, transport and housing, it is in these areas that they are most likely to make a grant. Your Parish council may issue grants to a limited range of local issues. If this is an area you are interested in pursuing, then make sure you do your research first.

Find out what links, if any, your branch may have or previously had with any statutory authorities, or whether any of your trustees or members have good

Arts appeal

The Dudley Autistic Support Group was successful in their bid for a £5000 grant from the National Lottery Small Grants Scheme, to run arts based activities for children with autism. Their original proposal had to show evidence of the children at work and play, and demonstrate how the children would benefit in the future from an arts-based programme. The bid itself involved a lot of detailed research and a well presented application, but on receiving the award, the Group realised that they hadn't really prepared for administering the funding. They didn't have a committee in place and they needed to ensure that additional fundraising was actioned. Most importantly that the group needed to be accountable for the grant provision.

A committee was duly set up to ensure 'best practice' and to oversee the spending of the grant. A number of other initiatives such as jumble sales, collections and local appeals were also organised to boost funds further, and the group not only gained monetarily but also increased publicity and awareness of their project. Fifty children with autism and their siblings enjoyed a trip to the theatre, to regular music performances and a visit to the local glassworks, leaving with a glass paperweight of their handprints.

"Raising funds has also enabled the group to run subsidised social events for parents and fun events for all the family as well as providing parent support" said Ian Attfield of the Dudley Autistic Support Group. "As a result of the publicity surrounding the Group's work, the Halesowen Ladies Circle nominated the NAS as their charity of the year, which has resulted in a sizeable donation to the Society."

Funding

links with any likely local sources of funds. Also find out about possible funders and try to match specific projects to them. Approach other funders to discuss their needs and find out the best way to present your application. Ensure that you put together a full proposal and find out how it needs to be submitted: on an application form or in a detailed letter.

Please note that the NAS Fundraising team co-ordinates all approaches across the UK to Charitable Trusts and foundations, the National Lottery Charities Board and to statutory funders like the Department of Health and the Welsh Office. You should check with the Fundraising Department before contacting any of these bodies.

Planning ahead

Plan your event at least 6 months beforehand, compile a timetable of action and keep things as simple as possible. Find out if you need permission to use the venue and check with the local authority if necessary. Strict rules about the preparation and sale of food are also in force. Check with the council's Environmental Health Department or use a licensed caterer if you can afford it. Find out if the venue has a liquor licence. You may need a public entertainment licence for music or live performance.

Do not forget insurance. You can obtain one-off policies for public liability and pleuvious insurance. If the public is attending your event and they have an accident, you are liable and public liability insurance will cover this eventuality. An insurance broker can give you advice. It might also be worth taking out a wet weather plan.

Organisation

Budget for your event, listing all expenditure against potential income. Be realistic in your approach and this will come in useful when planning future events. Good common sense and planning will help to ensure your event is a success. Be ruthless and weed out all the non-essential items and if necessary shop around for the cheapest suppliers.

Planning to hold a larger sponsored event will take a little careful organisation and you may need to alert management/authorities if a large number of people are going to be involved at the same time.

Careful consideration should also be given to more risky pursuits. There are many reputable companies who specialise in areas such as bungee jumping or parachuting. They are insured and will be able to help you – so don't take any unnecessary risks.

Funding

If your event is sponsored, make sure you take along a friend or partner to verify that you completed the route you had been sponsored to do. When asking people to sponsor you, stick to those you know and you are likely to have more success. Set a date when all monies should be collected.

Generating awareness

Get some publicity for your event by informing the local newspaper or tourist office, for example, and try and ensure that nothing similar is happening in the vicinity. If no-one knows your event is happening, the turnout will be poor and everyone will be disgruntled. Poor advertising or publicity can let down the best organised events and result in few funds being raised, so there are some important things to remember.

Despite the increase in autism awareness, don't presume that there is wide knowledge about the subject. When you talk to donors you need to assume ignorance on their part, so give them just enough information about the appeal and tell them what project you are helping or intending to fund through their donations.

Write a press release and send it to your local newspaper. Ring the paper first to find out the name of the person to send it to, and ask them if they can use photographs or are interested in sending a photographer along on the day, Contact the NAS Fundraising Department or Press Office for a guide to publicising your events. Write to the editor of a local newspaper with details of your event, asking for their help; if your letter is published, it will be valuable free publicity. Send your press release to all local radio stations but don't forget hospitals and university radio too. If you're lucky, you may even be able to arrange a live broadcast from the event.

You could design and print bright, eye-catching posters to display in local areas. Flyers are inexpensive to produce and can be distributed cheaply in free papers or pushed through letterboxes to request things such as jumble. Ask your local printer or print shop for a quote.

Advertising is not always the most cost-effective option, although some publications offer reduced rates for charity events. A small ad in the 'What's on' section is invaluable. Keep information simple and concise and ensure it includes the date, time and place.

Sponsored tipple

The Suffolk branch organised a pub-crawl to coincide with Autism Awareness Week. Fancy dress was optional for a group of around 12 volunteers made up of branch members, friends and family who had all responded to an advertisement in the monthly newsletter. Ten pubs in Ipswich were visited and a swift pint (or a soft drink if preferred) was downed at each one, before moving on to the next hostelry. The event raised well over £300 for branch funds, with one individual collecting £100 in sponsorship money. Although the event was in essence quite a simple one, the organisers had to approach every pub beforehand to get permission to go ahead with the event and also the local council for permission to run a collection in the pubs during each 'drinking session'. Everyone involved had a great night out (despite a few headaches next morning), but it worked because it was well organised, and appealed to most people who enjoy a night down the pub. As the branch secretary added "Make the event as fun as possible and more people will turn up to take part as well as offer sponsorship. Also raising money for a specific event will create even greater interest and really help to boost funds."

Include the NAS logo on publicity materials and please ensure that all references read "The National Autistic Society" and "Registered as Charity no. 269425". Please contact the NAS Publications Department if you need any advice about using the logo, colours to chose (there are official NAS colours) or what else to include (design and use of logo guidelines are available).

On the day

Distribute the timetable to the committee and volunteers and have a pre-event meeting to run through everything, ensuring that everyone involved knows what is expected of them. Be prepared for minor hitches and have a contingency plan in place. If you have one, take along a mobile phone as well as a list of phone numbers for all suppliers, volunteers or performers. Give everyone helping out regular breaks, and make sure they get looked after with refreshments throughout the day. After the event, thank everyone for their hard work with a follow-up phone call or letter.

Funding

The Scottish Society for Autism seeks to ensure the provision of the best possible education, care, support and opportunities for people of all ages with autism in Scotland. The Society also seeks to support families, improve understanding of autism and to develop best practice amongst carers, professionals and society at large.

We will advise or work in partnership with Education Authorities, Social Work Departments, other Local Authority Departments - or any other agency dealing with autism or Asperger syndrome - to develop practical solutions and new facilities.

The Scottish Society for Autism is the leading provider of services for autism in Scotland, which include:

a residential school for children

educational assessment and advice for individual children and educational authorities

adult accommodation group homes and community homes

specialist adult training and day services

a volunteer befrienders' scheme

asperger syndrome support service

the only respite care centre for autism in the UK

nationwide community support services training services for carers and professionals

information, advice and consultancy, a members magazine and newsletter

SOME STATISTICS

- we employ approximately 400 staff in 8 Locations
- we have school places for 30 children (21 residential, 9 day places)
- we operate 14 community houses and associated day services for 101 adults
- we have a 12 bedded respite provision capable of serving a minimum of 156 clients per year
- 400 family support visits a year are made by our Community Support workers
- we have over 500 members - including parents and professionals
- an estimated 28,000 people in Scotland have autism, Asperger syndrome or related communication disorders requiring specialist help and provision

The Scottish Society for Autism
(formerly The Scottish Society for Autistic Children)

Head Office: Hilton House, Alloa Business Park, Whins Road, Alloa FK10 3SA

Email: autism@autism-in-scotland.org.uk
Website: www.autism-in-scotland.org.uk

Tel: (01259) 720044   Fax: (01259) 720051

Scottish Charity No: SC 009068

Want to know more?

Fundraising is what you make it - you can choose how to be involved and to what extent. If you want to know more, contact the NAS Fundraising Department in the first instance, and talk to your local authority or volunteer bureau who should be able to give you some advice and provide information about groups and courses in your vicinity. Some local councils even organise their own free courses, or alternatively you could contact organisations such as the Directory of Social Change who also run a number of courses for professionals and volunteers.

As well as providing courses and training you will also be able to get up to date information on the law and regulations concerning events. Try the local library, which will have a good range of books on fundraising or visit the internet for relevant websites. Don't forget other branches; you can always talk to them to find out what has worked well for them in the past. It's important to share ideas and experiences. Contact the Membership Secretary at the NAS who can put you in touch with other branches (email: membership@nas.org.uk).

You will no doubt have lots of ideas of your own, but if you want to do something and are stuck for an idea, call the NAS Fundraising Department for some suggestions (a detailed list is available). Also keep them informed about your events, how you went about organising it, how successful it was on the day, how much money you raised, lessons learnt and so on, and don't forget to tell your local branch about how the event went. Through your stories, you can encourage others to become more involved and raise money and awareness about autism at the same time.

The National Lottery runs a scheme called 'Millennium Festival Awards for All' which makes grants of between £500 and £5000 to small organisations. This scheme is separate from the Charities Board and application forms, which are simple to complete, can be obtained from the numbers listed below. If your group is a branch of the NAS you will need a letter of endorsement from us to accompany your application. This can be obtained from your regional Development Officer.

| England | ☎ 0845 600 2040 | Scotland | ☎ 0645 700 777 |
| Wales | ☎ 0345 273 273 | Northern Ireland | ☎ 01232 526571 |

Funding

Useful publications

Tried and tested ideas for raising money locally, small and medium-scale events, Sarah Passingham, Directory of Social Change, 1997, 2nd edition, £9.95, ISBN 1900360292.

Organising local events, Sarah Passingham, Directory of Social Change, £9.95, ISBN 1900360098.

The complete fundraising handbook, Sam Clarke, Directory of Social Change, 1997, 3rd edition, £14.95, ISBN 1900360098.

Practical fundraising, David Wragg, Piatkus Publishers Ltd, 1995, £9.95, ISBN 0907164668.

Writing better fundraising applications, Michael Norton and Mike Eastwood, Directory of Social Change and ICFM, £12.95, ISBN 0907164668.

Starting and running a voluntary group, Sally Capper, Judith Unell and Anne Weyman, National Council for Voluntary Organisations, ISBN 0719912490.

Useful contacts

NAS Fundraising Department
☎ 020 7903 3522, fax 020 7833 9666, fundraising@nas.org.uk

NAS Scotland Fundraising Department
☎ 0141 221 9286, fax 0141 221 8118, scotland@nas.org.uk

Directory of Social Change (conferences and workshops)
☎ 020 7209 5151, fax 020 7209 5049.

CAF (Charities Aid Foundation)
☎ 01732 520 000, fax 01732 520 001.

NCVO (National Council for Voluntary Organisations)
☎ 020 8987 9663.

Adult life

Day-to-day living

The NAS recently published *Independent living for adults with autism and Asperger syndrome* as a guide for families of people with autistic spectrum disorders. This outlines important issues, such as the European Charter for autism, as well as giving advice on having an active social life. Available from the NAS Publications Department for £4.50 plus postage and packaging, ISBN 1899280170.

It is important to remember that there is life beyond diagnosis and schooling. The NAS is making efforts to ensure that there is true support and service provision available from early years to later life. This can cover such things as the tertiary course being developed by the NAS and Glasgow Nautical College partnership, the growing network of parent support schemes and ensuring that there is access to the welfare benefit system. These topics are dealt with elsewhere in the Handbook.

Adult partnerships

Brenda Wall, Asperger Backup Campaign

Due to the past belief that people with Asperger syndrome would not have the social skills needed to cope with a partner relationship, their needs and those of their partners for support, information and understanding have only recently begun to be addressed.

It is now a well established and accepted fact that some people with Asperger syndrome are able to form adult relationships, marry and have children. Edward Ritvo and his team at UCLA have studied autism intensively since 1963. During the 1980s they identified married adults with Asperger

Adults

Autism Initiatives meets the needs of people with autism throughout the North West. Its services include:

A network of group homes
Day care provision
Peterhouse School
Outreach work
Information and a training programme for parents and professionals

Autism Initiatives can be contacted on:
0151 339 9500 (phone)
0151 330 9501 (fax)

or at:

7 Chesterfiled Road
Crosby
Liverpool
L23 9XL

contact@autism-initiatives

Registered Charity: 702632

syndrome. Their attention was drawn by the spouses who noted that their partners had symptoms similar to the children with autism who the team had diagnosed and were treating. A letter to the editor of the *Journal of Autism and Developmental Disorders* was published in 1988, and the scientific paper was published in medical literature in 1996.

At the end of the autistic spectrum where a person is able to work and make close relationships, Asperger syndrome can be a hidden disorder. It is usually only after a couple start living together that the signs become noticeable. For the partner with Asperger syndrome the challenge of trying to maintain an intimate relationship while not understanding why their partner is angry and upset can cause such stress that matters may become worse.

For the partner of a person with Asperger syndrome, their bewilderment at the puzzling behaviour of their spouse can cause deep distress and a breakdown in their health. Inevitably, this means that there is a high divorce rate amongst marriages where one partner has Asperger syndrome. Research in Holland suggests that this is as high as 80%, and hopefully recent research in the UK will be published this year.

It is obviously essential that to encourage relationships to continue, support to partners is given in the form of advice and guidance on coping strategies, information and understanding of how their spouse is affected, and emotional support from other partners. Many partners live in fear that their spouse's employer will find out and dismiss them. For the partner with Asperger syndrome, there is as yet little help available. For those who express the wish for a formal diagnosis, it is often extremely difficult to find competent clinicians who are able to diagnose Asperger syndrome in adults. GPs usually insist on referral first to local services who do not have the necessary knowledge or experience. No way has yet been found of explaining to a person with Asperger syndrome, in a way they can comprehend, why their behaviour causes such hurt and upset in their partner.

There is also a great need for counsellors who have a thorough understanding of Asperger syndrome. Many couples have in the past been to Relate and received inappropriate advice, but Coventry Relate (01203 225863) now have one counsellor thoroughly qualified to help and Derby Relate have a telephone helpline (01332 345678) every Tuesday from 10.30am to 4.30pm

Adults

where the counsellors have received special training in Asperger's syndrome. The demand for these services will prompt the training of more counsellors.

The NAS have a factsheet *Help for partners of people with Asperger's syndrome* and their Regional Development Officers have partners' lists, contacts and hold meetings for partners. There is now an organisation in the USA called FAAAS (Families of Adults Afflicted with Asperger's Syndrome) and their website www.faaas.org has a wealth of helpful information with a mailing list which partners can join. Many people with Asperger syndrome have difficulty relating to babies and children and in understanding their needs.

Dr Tony Attwood held the first ever workshop for partners in March 1999 at the London head office of the NAS, and another workshop has been arranged for Tuesday 2 May 2000 when Dr Attwood next visits the UK. This workshop (cost £10) will be held in Coventry to enable more partners from the north of England, Scotland and Wales to attend. Application forms are available from the NAS website and also the FAAAS website. A transcript of the March workshop is available on the NAS and also the FAAAS websites. Dr Attwood has suggested that conferences concerning adults with Asperger syndrome should include programme relationship issues and help for partners in the programme.

References

Ratey, J.J. and Johnson, C. *Shadow syndromes*, Bantam Press, 1997.

Ritvo E. *et al.* (1988) *Eleven possibly autistic parents*, Letter to the editor, *Journal of Autism and Developmental Disorders* 18:139-143.

FAAAS (Families of Adults Afflicted with Asperger's Syndrome) website www.faaas.org

Practical strategies in the workplace: employment support workers at Prospects

Gill Spence and Justin Penney, Prospects Employment Support Workers

Introduction

Prospects is the NAS' employment initiative, helping adults with Asperger syndrome to find and retain work. With help and support from Prospects many people have obtained positions and gone on to become valued employees working in a range of different areas, such as computer programming, administration, clerical, warehouse and technician work. At present, Prospects covers the London and Glasgow areas, and it is hoped the service will expand to other areas of Britain in the future.

People who are registered with Prospects receive help and support from an employment support worker who is able to assist with the job-finding process and to provide support in the workplace once a job offer has been made. In a new job the support worker can be a source of support not only for the individual with Asperger syndrome, but also for managers and colleagues.

This chapter is intended for those with Asperger syndrome and but also for those who may work alongside or within the same organisation as someone with Asperger syndrome, either now or in the future. There are examples of some areas which may prove difficult for the individual with Asperger syndrome at work, and strategies that have been successfully used by support workers at Prospects.

Adults

Structuring the day

Some people with Asperger syndrome find it difficult to plan out their day and cannot see how they can 'fit' all the work tasks they have been assigned to do into a timeframe. To overcome this it is helpful to plan a timetable or 'breakdown' of the day, into smaller sections so the individual has a visual cue as to how the day can be planned out.

Managing breaks and lunchtimes

Often employees with Asperger syndrome will find breaks and lunchtimes more difficult to manage than the actual work tasks they are employed to do. This is because these times are usually unstructured, 'social' times, when colleagues may chat, laugh and relax over coffee or lunch. For someone with Asperger syndrome this type of social interaction is exactly the area where skills may be lacking or they may be unsure exactly what is expected of them.

Providing some guidelines on how to make 'small talk', for example providing a list of some key 'opening' phrases which can be used to start a conversation with colleagues during breaktimes, can prove helpful for someone with Asperger syndrome. Alternatively, for some people with Asperger syndrome, introducing some 'structure' to breaks and lunchtimes can help them to cope. Some suggestions could be to bring in a book or magazine to read, go for a short walk each day after lunch, do a crossword or puzzle book, or even to listen to a personal stereo.

Appropriate topics of conversation

Sometimes people with Asperger syndrome may say or ask things which colleagues may judge to be inappropriate, too personal, odd or even bizarre. It is important to be aware that this is not done on purpose to annoy or upset other people but merely based on a lack of understanding about 'accepted rules of conversation'.

It may be necessary to provide the person with Asperger syndrome with a list of inappropriate topics of conversation for the workplace, alongside a list of appropriate topics. It is important when telling people with Asperger syndrome what not to do, to also tell them what they could do instead. The list below is a suggestion of what this may look like.

Inappropriate topics of conversation:
1. Age. Asking people how old they are.
2. Money. Asking how much people earn, or how much their house, car or programmes cost.
3. Appearance. Commenting on others.
4. Personal life. Asking about people's marriages or relationships.
5. Personal hygiene issues.

Appropriate topics of conversation:
1. Asking people if they had a good weekend or holiday.
2. Music, films, theatre, books, TV programmes.
3. Shared interests and hobbies.
4. Work. Asking others about their role in the company, what they do and how long they have worked for the company etc.
5. The weather.

Obsessions and rituals

Many people with Asperger syndrome have obsessions and/or rituals, which are part of their everyday life. This is fine unless the obsession or ritual affects their work, upsets or irritates their colleagues. If this happens then some strategies will have to be introduced to overcome any problems. For example, one person who had a tendency to pace up and down the office was helped to incorporate this pacing into, 'pretending to go and pick something up from the printer' or 'walk to the toilets and back'.

Another person, who talked obsessively about dog racing to the point where his colleagues were extremely bored and frustrated, was set clear boundaries about when it was acceptable to talk about dog racing and when it was not (for 5 mins when he first arrived at work, 5 mins at the end of the day and at no other times during the working day). Through briefing his colleagues, reminding him of the boundaries, and providing immediate feedback if he did not stick to the boundaries, a pattern was established which was satisfactory to both the person with Asperger syndrome and his colleagues.

Making explanations and expectations clear

This is an area that people with Asperger syndrome may have difficulties in initially grasping. Many jobs have different expectations attached to them; they could be social or work-related. For instance, in an office environment the members of a team may take it in turns to get drinks for everybody. This is obviously not written into the specific duties of a position but is accepted by all as an 'unwritten rule' within the team. Somebody with Asperger syndrome may not take their turn, as it is not in their job description. This could cause a misunderstanding amongst colleagues as the person's unwillingness to take part may be interpreted as 'unsociable'. At Prospects we find that explaining these 'unwritten' rules can result in somebody with Asperger syndrome integrating easier into a team. Remember to make explicit what is implicit.

Adults

This also applies to giving instructions in the workplace. When giving instructions and/or explanations it is imperative to make sure you are clear and concise. Your instructions should also be as specific as possible, avoiding generalisations whenever possible. It is also important to be aware that verbal instructions alone may not always be adequate and are best backed up with some form of written guidelines. It may also be beneficial to get the employee to repeat back what they have just been shown. You may have to reinforce what you have explained over a period of time until you are satisfied that the employee has totally assimilated the instructions fully.

Organisation in the workplace

Many people with Asperger syndrome have difficulties in organising themselves effectively in the workplace. They may have problems recognising the advantages of working in an organised environment or indeed not know how to go about organising their time or workspace. For many people, written guidelines can be very helpful. For example, a written checklist of stationery required can reduce the amount of 'clutter' in the draws of a workstation. It may not be apparent to somebody that they do not need three staplers and that one would be sufficient. Also, helping somebody to organise his or her workspace can help to reduce stress, lead to more efficient working and present an altogether more professional image. It may also be helpful to put into place some form of monitoring system in order to enable the person to maintain an appropriate level of organisation.

Working file and troubleshooting guide

This is a very useful resource or strategy for somebody in work that has been proven to promote a good level of independence in the workplace. Some people with Asperger syndrome are prone to overchecking and asking numerous questions relating to tasks that may already have been explained. This amount of questioning is not to be taken as a measure of how much the person has learnt but rather the clients need to check that they are doing their job properly. As this constant questioning can be both distracting and time consuming, a preventative strategy is often the best way forward for all concerned.

As discussed above, people with Asperger syndrome can benefit immensely from written instructions. A typical working file could contain any amount of information, from lists of people's extension numbers to procedures for filing documents. As some questions may be asked again and again it might be a good idea to get the person to write down the answer in their file as you give it. If the question is asked again you can then redirect them to the file. This form of support is a useful tool for cutting interruptions down and can also promote confidence in the individual. Over a period of time the person will begin to become familiar with the information in the file and also will refer to the file first before asking questions. There is no limit to the amount of information which can be stored in these files and it can be constantly updated as and when problems arise.

Feedback

This is an integral part of the supervision process needed when working with somebody with Asperger syndrome. Line managers and colleagues need to be prepared to give feedback which is honest, consistent and constructive. As people with Asperger syndrome are not as proficient at reading social cues and picking up the 'unwritten' rules of the workplace, they will assume that their performance is acceptable unless explicitly told.

For example, if the person with Asperger syndrome makes a comment which is unacceptable, it is essential that the individual is discreetly told, in a clear and calm manner, what is inappropriate and what they could do instead. (It is preferable that this is addressed at the time or soon after the event.) This is a difficult area to tackle, but giving feedback which is not honest does not assist the client with their social skills. As you get to know the individual you will realise how helpful this can be to them.

Part of the support worker's role is to ensure that the line manager and employee meet on a regular basis for feedback on the employee's performance. From the outset of the individual obtaining a job the support worker will set up a weekly meeting for this specific purpose. It is important that these sessions remain an integral part of the person's development throughout their employment life.

Conclusion

This chapter is by no means exhaustive. It must be stressed that what works for one person will not necessarily work for another. People with Asperger syndrome are highly individual, the same as everybody else, and therefore need to be treated as such.

Adults

Know your rights

Compiled by Richard Wynn,
NAS Publications Department

Introduction

The NAS knows that many people with autistic spectrum disorders and their families benefit from having an official diagnosis. Having an explanation for the problems that a person has been experiencing, possibly for many years, can bring a sense of relief both for the parent and sometimes for the person themselves. It also provides ammunition to argue for the most appropriate support and services.

When discussing appropriate support and services it is important that you are also aware of your rights. This chapter gives an outline of how to go about accessing the support and services you have a right to: focusing on getting a diagnosis, the assessment and statementing of Special Educational Needs (SEN), and welfare benefits.

It is important to note that this is only a guide and not a comprehensive account. Individual cases vary greatly and many people find they come across different hurdles while getting a diagnosis, having their child assesssed and statemented, and getting welfare benefits. This chapter is designed to help, and the contacts and references given will often be able to offer more specific advice.

Getting a diagnosis

Getting a diagnosis can be a struggle. The recent *Opening the door* report (NAS 1999) highlighted how 40% of parents questioned waited more than 3 years to gain a diagnosis for their child, with 10% waiting 10 years or more. If getting a diagnosis does become a struggle, it is important to be prepared and armed for this.

Rights

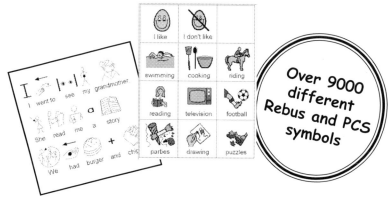
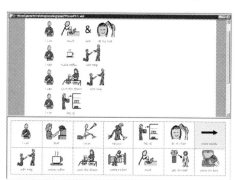

Children with autistic spectrum disorders can normally be diagnosed at around the age of 2 years. In many instances, professionals may spot tell-tale signs via normal childhood health checks and this can result in a formal diagnosis. If this does not happen and you feel there is a possibility that your child may have an autistic spectrum disorder, there are various steps you can take.

Unfortunately, some people, especially those at the more able end of the autistic spectrum, are sometimes not diagnosed until they are in their late teens, twenties, thirties and beyond. If you feel that you or a member of your family might have an autistic spectrum disorder, your right and route to diagnosis is exactly the same as that of a child (as listed below), whatever your age or circumstances.

Steps to take

If you think that your child may have an autistic spectrum disorder you need to see someone who has an in-depth knowledge of autistic spectrum disorders. The first step on the sometimes seemingly endless diagnostic road is to consult your GP who will usually refer your child to a local health professional. Typically, this will be a paediatrician (for children) or a psychiatrist (for children and adults).

A list of professionals you may come into contact with is provided in the leaflet *Important facts about autism and Asperger syndrome for GPs*, which is available from the NAS Publications Department (☎ 020 7903 3595). For further guidance on the kind of health professionals you might see during the diagnostic process, contact the NAS Autism Helpline ☎ 0870 600 85 85.

Under the Patients Charter (1991) you can request to see the professional of your choice. Under the Charter you can also seek a second opinion if you are not satisfied with the assessment or if the local health professional is unable to clearly identify why your child has difficulties. However, where you go for this second opinion is only negotiable between you and your local professional or GP.

Specialist centres, such as Elliot House, can only accept referrals from other professionals, usually GPs, paediatricians, psychiatrists and psychologists. Therefore, the parent who wishes to attend a particular centre needs to go

Rights

The Kent Autistic Trust

14 High Street, Brompton, Gillingham, Kent, ME7 5AE.
Tel: 01634 405168   Fax: 01634 811282

The Kent Autistic Trust is a registered charity, a non-profit making organisation that is a company limited by guarantee. It is affiliated to the National Autistic Society (NAS).

The Trust was started in 1985 by parents to provide a specialist service to respond to the needs of people with autism and their families. Membership is open to families, friends, staff and other individuals or professionals interested in autism.

The aims of the Trust are:
* To develop specialised residential homes and day support facilities for people with autism.
* To provide support and advocacy services for people with autism and their families.
* To identify and represent all people with autism in Kent.
* To define their needs and stimulate services to fulfil those needs.
* To develop the individual towards increasing confidence, independence, integration and control over their own life.

The Trust offers 52-week-a-year residential support within small homes for up to six people. We endeavour to create a family environment with residents taking part in all aspects of the running of the home whatever their ability. All homes are Registered with the local authority and inspected on a yearly basis with the conclusions available to the public.

Our three resource centres are separately based from the residential homes to create a working atmosphere during the week day. From the resource centres people participate in a wide range of skill training, work placement and therapy.

Our future plans are:
* To continue to improve the service provided to the people with autism currently supported by the residential and day service.
* To develop home and day services to meet identified need.
* To build on our services to families.
* To work towards extending our range of services to encompass a wider spectrum of support needs.

Contact Name: Kay Brunning, General Manager

back to their local professional or GP and ask him/her to refer them to this centre.

Referral problems often occur when a parent and not the professional involved suspects that the child concerned may have an autistic spectrum disorder. A 'catch 22' situation can develop where the local professional rules out, or does not consider that an autistic spectrum disorder is a possibility and refuses to refer. Due perhaps either to financial constraints or a lack of knowledge about autistic spectrum disorders, some GPs are unwilling to refer people on. Unfortunately, you have few legal rights in this situation.

If you are having problems getting your local professional or GP to refer your child, try contacting either the NHS information freephone number (☎ 0800 665544), who will be able to advise about your rights and complaints procedures as contained in the Patients Charter, or your Community Health Council (numbers will be in the phonebook), who should be able to advise on problems you may be having with local services.

It is advisable to try not to get into conflict with your GP. Being assertive and persistent with your GP will help. However, it is understandable that parents become frustrated if they do not get a referral. Some parents find it hard to be assertive with their GP, sometimes for fear of being 'struck off' by the practice. This can be a particular worry for parents who live in more isolated areas, where there is only one GP, or if they have more than one child and so do not want to jeopardise the relationship they have with their GP. You might find the following tips useful.

Useful tips
Support groups and helplines are a great source of information. The NAS Autism Helpline can be contacted on ☎ 0870 600 85 85, or for information about local support groups contact the NAS Information Centre ☎ 020 7903 3599.

Other parents that have been through the diagnostic process may also have valuable information regarding what you can expect from various professionals and assessment centres. If you have concerns about approaching your own GP, other parents may know of a good 'autism friendly' GP you could approach. You could also try seeing another GP based within your local practice.

Rights

Do not necessarily tell the professional what condition you think your child may have. If the professional rules this out, a conflict situation can develop where the parent is insisting that it is and the professional insists that it is not. It is advisable to avoid getting into this kind of conflict.

Clearly and concisely explain your child's difficulties. Find the common ground between you and the professionals. If your child has social difficulties explain them to the professional and ask if they agree. You and the professional can then establish and agree that your child does have social difficulties.

Your goal is to encourage the professional to acknowledge what your child does and does not do. Once the professional understands how your child behaves, he or she may be able to make the connection between your child's difficulties and the autistic spectrum.

If you are having problems convincing your GP, you may want to try and present your argument in a different way. Provide your GP with leaflets such as *Important facts about autism and Asperger syndrome for GPs*. You could also try matching the behaviours of your child to those outlined in this leaflet and/or keep a diary to record any unusual behaviours exhibited by your child and how often they occur (see the NAS Focus on the Family Booklet 4 *Experiences of the whole family*).

Get other professionals to tell your local professional or GP about your child's difficulties. If any professional involved (e.g. at school, health visitor or social worker) has shared their concerns with you, ask them to put it in writing to you and your GP or the specialist involved. Unfortunately, professionals often take more notice of other professionals than parents.

Do not accept the view of some professionals that they do not wish to label your child. A clear diagnosis can be a passport to the provision that your child needs.

Do not accept a partial diagnosis of autistic tendencies, traits, features or behaviours. Many parents are told that their child is not autistic but has autistic tendencies. This can restrict access to the help and support needed. Once the professional mentions autism you can push for him or her to agree that the child does have an autistic spectrum disorder.

Do not accept that your child's learning difficulties are causing him or her to behave in autistic ways. Many children with an autistic spectrum disorder do have learning difficulties, others have average abilities and some high intelligence. A child's intelligence level has nothing to do with whether they are within the spectrum or not.

Do not accept an alternative diagnosis if you believe there is more to your child's problems than the diagnosis suggests. For example, at Elliot House children have been diagnosed with an autistic spectrum disorder who have come with a previous diagnosis of chromosome abnormality, Down's syndrome, attention deficit hyperactivity disorder (ADHD), attention deficit disorder (ADD), emotional and behavioural problems, obsessive compulsive disorder, semantic pragmatic disorder, pervasive developmental disorder, challenging behaviour, learning difficulties, language disorder, conduct disorder, oppositional defiance disorder, pathological demand avoidance, parent/child relationship problems, and schizophrenia.

This does not mean that all children with these disorders are within the autistic spectrum. It is possible for a child to have more than one condition. Also, some conditions, such as obsessive compulsive disorders, can be a part of an autistic spectrum disorder. Some of the above conditions or explanations could have been given inaccurately.

If you are told that your child has any form of autism, including Asperger syndrome, he or she will need a written diagnosis. A clear diagnosis is when a professional writes that the child has an 'autistic spectrum disorder' (autism and Asperger syndrome are autistic spectrum disorders). Those are the key words that can be a passport for your child to access the help, support and understanding that they need.

Unfortunately, many parents find that obtaining a clear diagnosis for their child does take time. This can be incredibly frustrating, especially waiting months between appointments. It is important to take one step at a time and try to keep moving along the diagnostic road. If those involved acknowledge that your child has difficulties then you will have a stronger case to be referred on.

Rights

If you do come to a dead end, and everyone refuses to refer to a specialist, ask the professionals what they intend to do about establishing the cause of your child's difficulties. If your child does not have a clear diagnosis, ask those involved where they plan to send your child for a further diagnostic assessment.

You may find you have to become a persuasive diplomat to get your child's needs met. Often parents find that demanding and arguing does not get results. Do not give up and do not try to cope with the difficulty alone. Use support groups and keep knocking on doors until you achieve your objective. Trust your instincts – no one will know your child better than you.

Formal assessments and statementing

If you are the parent of a child and have concerns about how they are developing you can ask your LEA to assess your child's educational needs. This is done in the form of an assessment and then possible 'Statement of Needs'. In Scotland this is known as a 'Record of Needs'.

There are quite a few differences between the assessment and statementing processes in England and Scotland. ENABLE have produced a booklet The *Record of Needs – a guide for parents of children with special educational needs* which answers many of the questions parents in Scotland will have. Contact ENABLE for a copy ☎ 0141 226 4541 or enable@enable.org.uk.

It is worth starting off along the road towards an assessment and possible statement with a copy of the *Code of Practice for Special Educational Needs* (DfEE 1994). The Code gives guidance to LEAs – and will also be a guide and reference for you – during the process. If you would like to obtain a copy telephone the DfEE ☎ 0207 510 0150.

In Scotland, Local Education Department guidance comes from the Scottish Office circular *Children and young people with Special Educational Needs (Assessment and Recording)*. Contact The Scottish Office ☎ 0131 556 8400 for a copy.

Special educational needs

Every child has the right to an education which meets their individual needs. Special education needs exists when a child has a 'learning disability/difficulty' which calls for special educational provision.

One initial problem you may notice is that at present 'autistic spectrum disorder' is not specifically mentioned in the Code of Practice. This can, and does, lead to children with autistic spectrum disorders being classified under a general heading of 'learning disability/difficulty', which may not ensure they receive the most suitable support. If 'autistic spectrum disorder' was mentioned as a specific condition in any revision of the Code of Practice, it would greatly assist in ensuring that children received support and education appropriate to their needs. This should happen, after pressure from the NAS, when the revised edition is released in 2001.

It is important to remember that an official diagnosis is not itself a criterion for an LEA to determine the special educational provision needed to meet your child's needs. However, during the assessment and statementing process how you use an official diagnosis is the key. During the process a diagnosis of an 'autistic spectrum disorder' can provide a framework for arguing for correct provision. It can be used to present information about the difficulties your child has been diagnosed as having in a coherent way, by matching those difficulties to the kind of provision you want your child to receive.

The assessment and statementing process

The Code of Practice sets out five 'parts' in assessing the educational needs of any child thought to have special requirements.

Part 1: proposal to assess
The decision whether to assess your child, or not, is made by your LEA. Local Education Authorities can come to this decision in three ways: either you (the parent) can request an assessment, a referral can come from your child's school or agency, or a request can come from a grant-maintained school that has been asked to admit your child.

Rights

Authorities have a duty to identify children aged between 2 - 19 years whose SEN may make it necessary for them to provide special educational provision. It is only for children aged between 2 - 19 years that the process of assessing a child and then possibly providing a statement takes a prescribed form. Statements for children aged under 2 years can be made in any form.

How you can make a formal request for an assessment?

You must write to your LEA Education Officer and ask for them to assess the educational needs of your child under Section 167 of the 1993 Education Act. It is your right to request an assessment under Section 172 of the Act, if your child already has a statement, or 173 of the Act, if your child has no statement.

Parents can request an assessment of their child if they do not already have a statement of SEN or if they wish for a reassessment. The LEA must assess your child unless an assessment has either been made within the previous 6 months or if the LEA does not consider an assessment is necessary. If the LEA decides an assessment is unnecessary it may not give specific reasons for the decision. What an LEA must do is inform you of your appeal rights. If you are unhappy with the decision you are legally entitled to a right of appeal and this can be made to a SEN Tribunal.

Once you have requested an assessment, an LEA must inform you of their decision within 6 weeks. This time limit, as set out in the Code of Practice, can only be extended under exceptional circumstances.

SEN Tribunal

During certain 'parts' of the assessment and statementing process you have the right to appeal to an SEN Tribunal, for example if the LEA refuses to assess your child or if they refuse to issue a statement after the assessment. An LEA should inform you of your right to appeal and how to go about this.

In Scotland, appeals are made to either the Education Authority Appeals Committee or to Scottish Ministers, depending on the nature of the appeal. Appeal Committee decisions can be appealed to the Sheriffs Court, but their decision is final.

When an LEA makes a proposal to assess

If a request for an assessment comes from either your child's school, other agency or a grant-maintained school that has been asked to admit your child, an LEA must inform you of the proposal in a formal notice.

A formal notice should set out the following:

- The assessment procedure and your role in it.
- Who the LEA intend to consult during the assessment.
- A 'Named Officer' – an LEA representative who you can go to for further information.
- Your right to a 'Named Person' who you can got to for independent help and advice, and where to get this.
- Information on a full range of educational provision in mainstream and special schools within the LEA.
- Your right to make representations, 'parental representations', about the proposal to assess (this must be done within 29 days of receiving the notice).

The LEA will wait to hear from you within the 29 days, about whether you agree with the proposal to assess or not, before deciding whether to proceed with the assessment. In having 29 days to respond to your LEA you will have some time to find out about the assessment and why it is being proposed. You may wish to write to, or meet with, your Named Officer at this point in time to discuss the proposal.

Putting your case to the LEA

It is entirely up to you and relevant to your situation as to whether you are gathering information to back up your case for an assessment and suitable statement or if you are opposing a proposal to assess your child. Either way, if you have requested an assessment or if an LEA has informed you that they wish to assess your child, you must start to gather information which will strengthen your case.

Parental representations

It is important to gather 'parental representations', information about your child to back up your case. These representations should be obtained from your own doctor, teachers, social workers and even friends, for example. You should get them to put their views in writing so you can send them to your LEA when you respond within the 29-day limit.

Rights

Named Person

You can also get independent advice and help from a Named Person during the assessment and statementing process. A Named Person plays the role of an adviser. You can choose your own Named Person or not have one if you so wish. However, it is advisable to have a Named Person from the start of the assessment procedures as they will be able to play a full part, and offer accurate and independent advice throughout.

Educational provision

You may have concerns that after an assessment the LEA will suggest a special school placement, whereas you may want your child to remain in a mainstream school. Under the Education Act (1980) a parent has a right to express a preference for a particular school and to appeal against a placement. You can state your preference for a particular school and appeal if you are refused a place there. If your child already has a statement, parental preference is covered by the Education Act (1993).

Need more time

If you are opposing a proposal to assess your child you can write to the LEA, within the 29-day limit, and request more time. You must, however, give reasons as to why you may need this.

There is no statutory right of appeal against an LEA's decision to actually undertake a formal assessment and so it is important to present a strong case before they make this decision if you do not wish them to assess your child.

Part 2: the LEA decide

Once you have made a request for an assessment or have responded to your LEA's proposal to assess, within the 29-day period, they should then inform you in writing of their decision.

Part 3: the assessment

There is a 10-week statutory time limit within which an LEA must complete an assessment. The Code of Practice gives clear guidance on assessment procedures which are in fact governed by law under the Education (Special Educational Needs) Regulations (1994). An LEA must, as a minimum, take into account six sources of advice when undertaking an assessment. These advisers are:

1. The child's parents, including any 'parental representations'. An LEA should also provide parents with a pro forma set of questions you can complete to help you contribute to the assessment effectively. LEAs are also advised to encourage parents and their Named Person to seek the views of the child themselves.

2. Educational. Normally sought from your child's current headteacher.

3. Medical. Must be sought from the District Health Authority, who obtain advice from a registered medical practitioner. The LEA must inform you in writing of any medical tests. It is within your rights to attend any tests and if you are dissatisfied with the tests, record any reasons why.

4. Psychological. Must be sought from a person employed as an educational psychologist by the LEA or involved as such in the case. The LEA must inform you in writing of any psychological tests. It is within your rights to attend any tests and if you are dissatisfied with the tests, record any reasons why.

5. Social Services Department.

6. Any other which the LEA considers appropriate.

The management of these six advisers can vary from one LEA to another. For information on this, and if you are concerned about the role of any of the advisers, you should ask your Named Officer for details. It is essential that all advisers provide as detailed information as possible about your child - and you should encourage them in this role as well as providing detailed 'parental representations' yourself.

Part 4: the proposed statement
From the date when an assessment is completed, an LEA must send you a copy of the proposed statement within 2 weeks. An LEA must also follow detailed guidance on what is included in a statement, under these headings as advised by the DfEE:
- Child – details of your child, i.e. name, address.
- Special Educational Needs – the LEAs view on your child's SEN.
- Special Educational Provision, Objectives, educational provision to meet needs and objectives, monitoring - provision the LEA deems appropriate.

Rights

Gloucestershire Group Homes

*Small group homes in the community providing support
and training for adults with diagnosis of Asperger syndrome*

Spring Mill Business Centre
Avening Road, Nailsworth, Glos   GL6 0BS
Tel: 01453 835023   Fax: 01453 836932

Gloucestershire Group Homes was established as an independent
voluntary organisation with charitable status in March 1994.
Previously, two of our five homes were incorporated in an
organisation that was originally set up by parents of children with
the diagnosis of autism in the 1980s.

During the past 3 years Gloucestershire Group Homes has
developed its service and has focused on providing an appropriate
environment and support system for those individuals with the
diagnosis of high functioning Autism/Asperger Syndrome.

The main aim of Gloucestershire Group Homes is to provide a
safe and caring environment that enables people to achieve their
fullest potential, taking into account the individual's intellectual,
physical, emotional and social abilities.

Supporting people to achieve as much independence in their lives
as possible is a priority of Gloucestershire Group Homes.

Gloucestershire Group Homes do not hold a "waiting list",
although we do take referrals and will contact individual requests
if and when a vacancy arises. Each individual will be assessed and
costed depending on needs.

For further information, please contact the manager at the above
address.

- Placement – the school the LEA deems appropriate. However, you have the right to name your preferred school. Home education may also be considered here.
- Non-educational needs.
- Non-educational provision.
- Appendices – should contain all parental representations and evidence, as well as the advice from the six sources outlined above.

Included in a statement, the LEA must inform you of your right to express a preference of school and to negotiate over the contents of the statement.

If the LEA decides not to statement your child, they must inform you of your right to appeal via the SEN Tribunal. An LEA may provide a 'Note in lieu' of a statement which will contain all the supporting evidence from the assessment. With the agreement of you and your child's school this can be discussed and used as guidance for helping your child. This will take co-operation from a school as they are not legally bound by a Note in lieu.

Checking the content of a proposed statement

From receipt of a proposed statement you only have 15 days to either make comments and challenges or request a meeting with an LEA Officer and any of the advisers as is your right under Schedule 10 of the Education Act 1993.

However, before any meetings it is worth checking the statement thoroughly. Go through each of the sections outlined above in detail:

- Are your child's details correct?
- Is the description of your child's SEN accurate? Does the description made here reflect the advice sought and outlined in the appendices? Any conflicting advice must be explained by the LEA.
- Does the proposed provision meet all the needs outlined in the description of your child? Is there anything you would like to see added? Has all the advice outlined in the appendices been considered? Are you satisfied with the overall proposed provision and does this reflect the provision you consider your child to need?
- Do you have enough information in order to consider where you would like your child to be placed? The LEA should have sent you details of all primary, secondary maintained and non-maintained schools. Did you

Rights

have this information early on in the assessment process, giving you enough time to visit these schools?

- If an LEA is proposing non-educational provision, are they going to provide this?

If you want to meet with any LEA Officers or advisers (whose information has been given in the assessment's appendices) regarding the proposed statement, you can arrange this. When meeting with an Officer it may be useful to have a list of questions, noted when going through the Statement.

After any meetings you should then send in your comments and any challenges to the LEA within 15 days.

Part 5: the formal statement

Within 8 weeks of issuing the proposed statement, the LEA must consider your challenges and comments, and then either make the statement of SEN or decide not to continue with the statement. If the latter option is chosen by the LEA you have the right to appeal to an SEN Tribunal. The LEA must inform you of this right and how to go about it.

Welfare benefits

There are a range of welfare benefits available to people with disabilities, and many of those with autistic spectrum disorders and their families may be entitled to claim them. Which benefits a person may be entitled to, and the amount they can claim, will depend on the degree of the person's autism and their individual circumstances. The key benefits are briefly listed below.

Disability Living Allowance (DLA)

Disability Living Allowance is a benefit available to children and adults with a disability who are under 65 years old. There are two components, one for help with personal care, which is payable at three different rates, and one for help with mobility, which is payable at two different rates.

Complete the DLA Claim Pack (DLA1), or for children DLA1 Child, available from your local DSS (Department of Social Security) office, Post Office or by ringing the Benefit Agency Enquiry Line ☎ 0800 882200.

A free fact sheet entitled *Claiming Disability Living Allowance* is available from the NAS Autism Helpline. Please send an SAE marked 'Claiming Disability Living Allowance' to NAS Autism Helpline, The National Autistic Society, 393 City Road, London EC1V 1NG.

Invalid Care Allowance (ICA)

Invalid Care Allowance is paid to people who spend at least 35 hours a week caring for a child who is receiving DLA at either the middle or higher rate.

Complete the ICA claim pack (DS700) available from your local DSS office, Post Office or by ringing the Benefit Agency Enquiry Line.

Severe Disablement Allowance (SDA)

Severe Disablement Allowance will be abolished in 2001. For details on how this may affect you, contact the Benefit Agency Enquiry line. SDA is for people over 16 who have not been able to work for at least 28 consecutive weeks because of illness or disablement.

Complete the application form in the Severe Disablement Allowance leaflet (N1252) available from DSS offices or by ringing the Benefit Agency Enquiry Line.

Disability Working Allowance (DWA)

Disability Working Allowance is designed to help disabled people top up their earnings. They have to be working at least 16 hours or more a week and be in receipt of one of a number of passport benefits.

Complete a DWA claim pack (DAW1) available from your local DSS office or ring freephone ☎ 0800 100123.

The Orange Badge Scheme

The Orange Badge Scheme is designed to allow people with disabilities to park close to shops or other places they need to visit. It also entitles them to a designated parking place outside their home, and free parking in metered areas and on yellow lines. An application form and explanatory leaflet about the scheme is available from your local DSS office. In Scotland you need to apply to the chief executive of your local regional or island council.

Rights

The InterACT Centre

c/o Hanwell Community Centre,
Westcott Crescent, London W7 1PD

Founded in 1994, *The InterACT Centre* is a non-residential further education college specialising in educating people with Asperger Syndrome funded by the Further Education Funding Council.

At the INTERACT Centre we are interested in the potential internal adaptions that students might be able to make in overcoming some of their difficulties.

During their time at INTERACT a student will have:
- Learnt the skills needed to progress onto a higher level course or training
- Develop some insight into themselves and how they interact. Developed some insight into how others see them.
- Develop some abilities in planning and organising themselves.
- Made use of other people more effectively e.g. problem solving and being helped.
- Recognising different states of mind (e.g. frustration) and how this might affect their ability to interact with other people.
- Develop realistic expectations about their futures and themselves.
- Recognised the need for dependence on others on the one hand and on the other more independent and more reliant on own initiative, knowledge and own experience.
- Be less reliant on being understood by others and make themselves understood.

In 1995 the work of InterACT was inspected by The Further Education Funding Council and described as *"... particularly effective in enabling students to learn to interact appropriately with other people."* (FEFC report 1995.) Next FEFC inspection is March 2000.

The InterACT Centre is also fully accredited by The National Autistic Society's Autism Network Quality Audit Scheme. *"The staff team have considerable theoretical knowledge and practical experience in the field of autism."* (Accreditation Report 1996.) The latest audit was in December 1999 - go to our website for the 2000 report.

For more up to date information see our website at:
www.jamesg.dircon.co.uk/InterACT

Principal: James E Graham
Tel: 020 8575 0046. E-mail: jamesg@dircon.co.uk

Motability

Motability is a scheme to help people with disabilities and those who care for them buy or hire a car. To qualify you must be receiving the DLA mobility component at the higher rate.

For further information contact: Motability, Gate House, West Gate, The High, Harlow, Essex, CM20 1HR, ☎ 01279 635999, Customer Services Helpline ☎ 01279 635666.

Vehicle Excise Duty

Vehicles used exclusively by a person receiving the higher rate of the DLA mobility component or kept solely for that purpose are exempt from Vehicle Excise Duty. You should automatically receive an application form if you qualify for DLA.

The Family Fund

The Family Fund is financed by the government and administered by the Joseph Rowntree Foundation. The Fund is for families with children under the age of 16 who are severely disabled. Grants can be made for items such as bedding, clothing, washing machines and holidays.

Applications should be made in writing giving the name and date of birth of the child, details about their disability, the kind of help they require, and whether you have applied to the Fund before. Contact: The Family Fund, PO Box 50, York YO1 2ZX.

Other sources of financial help

There are an enormous range of charitable organisations that you may be able to approach for a one-off grant. They vary greatly, both in terms of the amounts of money they have and their eligibility criteria. Some may only be open to people who live in a particular geographical region, others to those who have been employed in a particular profession.

A useful reference book to consult if you are looking for this kind of financial help is: *A guide to grants for individuals in need*, David Casson and Paul Brown (editors), £18.95, Directory of Social Change, ISBN 0 907164 86 2. You may be able to find a copy of this in the reference section of your local library.

Rights

Income Support

If your income falls below a certain level you may be able to claim Income Support, even if you are receiving other welfare benefits. If you qualify for Income Support you may also be entitled to a number of additional payments known as premiums. These include:

- Disability Premium, if you are yourself disabled and receiving one of a number of qualifying benefits.
- Severe Disability Premium, if you receive Attendance Allowance or DLA care component at the high or middle rate.
- Family Premium, if you have a dependent child aged under 19 years.
- Disabled Child Premium, if you have a child who receives DLA.
- Carer Premium, if you or your partner receive ICA, or would get it but for overlapping benefit rules.

Complete the slip on the Income Support leaflet (IS1) available from post offices or DSS offices and a claim form will be sent to you. Alternatively claim forms can be obtained from your local DSS office or by ringing the Benefit Agency Enquiry Line.

Housing Benefit

Housing benefit is paid by local councils to people who need help in paying their rent. The amount of housing benefit you may be able to claim will depend on any savings you may have, how much money you have coming in and the size of your family.

If you claim Income Support you will automatically get a form (NHB1) to claim Housing Benefit and Council Tax Benefit. If you do not receive Income Support or do but now want to claim Housing Benefit you should contact your local council.

Council Tax Benefit

If you are on a low income you may be able to get help from your local council in paying your Council Tax bill. The amount you can claim will depend on any savings you have, your income and personal circumstances. People with a disability or those that care for them may be able to qualify for a rebate. Also, you may be able to get a reduction in your Council Tax bill regardless of your income if your home is used by someone with a disability.

If you claim Income Support you will automatically get a form (NHB1) to claim Housing Benefit and Council Tax Benefit. If you do not receive Income Support or do but now want to claim Council Tax Benefit you should contact your local council.

The Social Fund

The Social Fund helps people with expenses which are difficult to pay out of regular income, such as clothing, bedding, laundry and equipment. These are made as grants or, more commonly, as loans.

Complete form SF300 available from your local DSS office.

Budgeting loans

These are designed to help people spread the cost of more expensive items such as a cooker, furniture or removal expenses, over a longer period. To qualify you must have been receiving Income Support for at least 26 weeks. The loans are interest-free but must be repaid. Any savings over a certain level must be used first. Complete form SF300 available from your local DSS office.

Crisis loans

Crisis loans are designed to help people who cannot meet their immediate short-term expenses in an emergency where there is a serious risk to health and safety of the family. Forms are usually filled in during an interview at the DSS office but if you wish to complete one at home ask for SF401.

These notes are based on those contained in the NAS leaflet Financial help, part of the pack _The autistic spectrum – a parent's guide_, which is available for £2.00 from the NAS Publications Department.

Rights

Focus on Disability Living Allowance

The most common enquiries regarding benefits the NAS' Autism Helpline receive are about claiming DLA.

DLA is a benefit available to help with personal care and/or getting around. It is available to children and adults with a disability under 65 years old. Many people have successfully claimed DLA because their child needs: help with, for example, washing, dressing or going to the toilet; someone to keep an eye on them during the day; someone to keep an eye on them at night; cannot get around outdoors without supervision; or has a severe mental impairment.

DLA will not affect any other benefits you claim. In fact it can mean you qualify for more Income Support, Benefit or Council Tax Benefit. Also, if you have any savings, this will not affect your DLA claim.

DLA can be awarded for anything from 1 year to life, comes in two parts: the care component and the mobility component. You can claim either or both components. DLA care is awarded at three rates: higher, middle and lower. DLA mobility is awarded at two rates: higher and lower.

Filling out the DLA1A form

Fill in a detailed application form specifically for children (DLA1A) available from your local DSS office, Post Office or Benefit Agency Enquiry Line. The form is specifically for children under 16 and asks for information about your child's care and mobility needs. Your application will be assessed by the DSS on the basis of the information you give. How you present your case is therefore very important. The person who assesses your application is unlikely to have detailed knowledge of autistic spectrum disorders. It is important to give them as much relevant information as possible, including examples from your own experiences.

Filling out benefits' forms can be a nightmare and it sometimes seems as though the forms are designed in such a way as to make it as difficult as it can be. The following tips may make the filling out of DLA forms a bit easier.

Rights

1. Always keep in mind why you are filling out the form, i.e. to give a picture of your child's **disabilities**, therefore no comical anecdotes.

2. Enlist the help of an outsider who knows your child. Remember you may take for granted all the help you give your child, and what's normal for the family with a child with an autistic spectrum disorder may be bizarre or unusual for others.

3. Keep a **detailed** diary of all the help you give your child. The diary should include headings relevant to the DLA form and act as a memory prompt to time or distances and other kinds of information that can be easy to forget.

A free guide Keeping a DLA diary by Jan Murdoch and Martine Ives is available from the NAS Autism Helpline, or you could look at Focus on the Family Booklet 3 How children learn behaviour.

4. Have a trial run. It will allow you to plan the most appropriate responses in the relevant places/sections. Once you get your brain into the DLA way of thinking, you may come up with more descriptive, succinct phrases, better examples, etc.

5. Keep a copy! This has a number of benefits, such as providing all the information relevant to your claim should you need to appeal or ask for a review. It will also be handy when the benefit award period ends and your claim will be renewed, since you have to fill a renewal form giving almost the same information all over again. It could also serve as a useful local resource for parent groups so that other parents can get an idea of what things to include.

6. Access additional help.
- The Claiming DLA Factsheet available from the Autism Helpline gives a brief general overview.
- Local Citizen's Advice Bureau, advice services, other professionals involved with your child, e.g. social workers, paediatrician, teacher, speech and language therapists. They could help with structuring and articulating your form. Check this out with them in advance to ensure they are in a position to help.

- If you're really stuck for where to start, then perhaps try your local NAS branch. Parents who have already filled out the form and succeeded could be valuable sources of information and help. As a Branch you could think about arranging DLA troubleshooting/brainstorming meetings inviting a local welfare rights worker or similar professional if possible. Also think about keeping a Branch library of example forms which have been successful. Obviously the personal details should be deleted.

- Always use your own words and those experiences which you can personally relate to your own situation.

- If your child is nearing the age of 5 years, hence potentially qualifying for the mobility component, you can make this application once your child reaches 4 years 9 months. However, do make sure you ask the Benefits Agency to look only at the mobility section, otherwise they may look at your whole award.

- If it is your first claim, phone the Benefits Agency Enquiry Line for your claim pack. Note that this is provided by the DSS and not an independent agency, thus you may not feel comfortable disclosing personal information to them. Your form, included in your claim pack, will be date-stamped from your initial request, which will ensure any award will be made from the earliest possible time.

- Do not be put off by the 'Additional Section'. This form is looking for information on the kinds of activities you/your child is enabled/would be enabled to do if you had the help you need.

- Don't worry if you have a strained relationship with your GP. You can ask that they do not see the form or be contacted for further information.

- Do follow the guidelines and add extra sheets for further information if you want. Compare it to a job application form, where a lot of information serves to give a fuller picture. Always refer back to your answers to previous questions when giving more information, to ensure you do not contradict yourself on any points. Plus, if you have additional sheets these must have your name and reference number (National Insurance or Child Benefit numbers) on it. If in doubt, put on your child's date of birth.

- Remember you are filling out the form for a very good reason. Individuals with autistic spectrum disorders have a disability and are therefore entitled to access disability benefits because of the extra pressures this can place on the family resources.

Rights

Further information

Getting a diagnosis

Patients Charter 1991. Copies available by calling the NHS Information free ☎ 0800 665544.

Important facts about autism and Asperger syndrome for GPs, NAS, 1999, £0.25, ISBN 1899280286

Larcombe, M. *What to do if you suspect your child may have an autistic spectrum disorder, Communication*, Winter 1998.

Assessment and statementing

The Code of Practice on Special Educational Needs, DfEE, 1994. Available from the DfEE ☎ 0207 510 0150.

Children and young people with special educational needs (assessment and recording), The Scottish Office, 1996, free of charge. Available from The Scottish Office, Education and Industry Department, Area 2a (West), Victoria Quay, Edinburgh EH6 6QQ or ☎ 0131 556 8400.

Special education handbook – the law on children with special needs, The Advisory Centre for Education (ACE), 1996. Available from ACE, 1b Aberdeen Studios, 22 Highbury Grove, London N5 2DQ or ☎ 0207 354 8318. ACE also have an advice line Monday to Friday, 2 - 5pm, ☎ 0171 354 8321.

The Record of Needs – a guide for parents of children with special educational needs, ENABLE, 1999, £19.99. Available from ENABLE, 6th Floor, 7 Buchanan Street, Glasgow G1 3HL or ☎ 0141 226 4541, enable@enable.org.uk.

Welfare benefits

Further information and guidance on claiming welfare benefits can be obtained by contacting your local CAB or Welfare Rights Unit (address in the phone book) or alternatively from:

Disability Alliance, 1st Floor, Universal House, 88 - 94 Wentworth Street, London E1 7SA. Rights Advice Line ☎ 0207 247 8763 Monday and

Wednesday 2 - 4p.m. fax 0207 247 8765.

Disability Benefit Enquiry Line (BEL) ☎ 0800 882200, Monday to Friday 8.30am - 6.30 pm and Saturday 9.00 am - 1.00 pm.

From claim to appeal: a guide to disability appeal tribunals for disabled people and their advisers, D. Dixon, Disability Alliance ERA, 1994.

Disability rights handbook, J. Paterson, 23rd edition, Disability Alliance ERA, 1998. Published annually by Disability Alliance ERA, Universal House, 88 - 94 Wentworth Street, London, E1 7SA.

*Claiming Disability Allowance factshee*t NAS. Contact the NAS Information Centre ☎ 0207 903 3599 for a free copy.

Keeping a DLA diary factsheet, Jan Murdoch and Martine Ives, NAS, 1999. Available from the NAS Autism Helpline ☎ 0870 600 85 85.

The autistic spectrum – a parent's guide, NAS 1999, £2, ISBN 1899280081. Available from the NAS Publications Department on ☎ 0207 903 3595. Includes information on recognising the signs and getting a diagnosis, education, financial help and further references.

Useful numbers

The NAS Autism Helpline ☎ 0870 600 85 85.

Benefits Agency Enquiry Line ☎ 0800 882200.

Rights

The National Autistic Society (NAS) Training Services Department

We are able to provide autism specific training for professionals, practitioners and carers throughout the UK. We are currently running a series of workshops and conferences on a range of topics. We also provide tailored in house training for statutory, voluntary and private organisations.

Forthcoming workshops and conferences include:

- **SPELL ONE** – A 1-day workshop on Autistic Spectrum Disorders and basic principles of SPELL.

  (SPELL is a Framework used in NAS schools and adults centres to maximise life and learning opportunities for children and adults with Autistic Spectrum Disorders).

- **SPELL TWO** – A 2-day workshop on putting SPELL into practice.

- **CONFERENCES** – A series of one-day Conferences on a range of topics. These include 'Issues in Diagnosis and Assessment' and 'Early Intervention'.

- **TEACCH** – A 3-day workshop on 'Structured Teaching Model: Basic Concepts'.

For further information, please contact The National Autistic Society, Training Department, 4th Floor, Castle Heights, 72 Maid Marian Way, Nottingham NG1 6BJ.
Tel: 0115 911 3363   Fax: 0115 911 3362
E-mail: training@nas.org.uk
Website: http://www.oneworld.org/autism_uk/

THE NATIONAL
AUTISTIC SOCIETY

Gazetteer

About The National Autistic Society

The National Autistic Society
393 City Road
London
EC1V 1NG
☎ 020 7833 2299
fax 020 7833 9666
nas@nas.org.uk
www.oneworld.org/autism_uk/

Autism Helpline	☎ 0870 600 8585
Fundraising	☎ 020 7903 3522
Information Centre	☎ 020 7903 3599
Press/PR	☎ 020 7903 3593
Prospects	☎ 020 7704 7450
Publications	☎ 020 7903 3595
Parent to parent support	☎ 0800 9 520 520
Volunteers network	☎ 0115 911 3369

NAS Northern Ireland
Queens University Belfast, 18-30 Malone Road, Belfast BT9 5BP
☎ /fax 028 9027 4547

NAS Scotland
Forsyth House, 2nd Floor, 111 Union Street, Glasgow G1 3TA
☎ 0141 221 8090, fax 0141 221 8118, fundraising ☎ 0141 221 9286,
scotland@nas.org.uk

NAS Wales
William Knox House, Suite C1, Britannic Way, Llandarcy, Neath SA10 6EL
☎ 01792 815915, fax 01792 815911, wales@nas.org.uk

Gazeteer

Services division - for NAS Schools and adult centres
Church House, Church Road, Filton, Bristol BS34 7BD
☎ 0117 987 2575, fax 0117 987 2576, services@nas.org.uk

Development and Outreach
4th Floor, Castle Heights, 72 Maid Marion Way, Nottingham NG1 6BJ
☎ 0115 911 3360, fax 0115 911 2259

Training
4th Floor, Castle Heights, 72 Maid Marion Way, Nottingham NG1 6BJ
☎ 0115 911 3363, fax 0115 911 3362, training@nas.org.uk

The Centre for Social and Communication Disorders
Elliot House, 113 Masons Hill, Bromley, Kent BR2 9HT
☎ 020 8466 0098, fax 020 8466 0118

Factsheets
The NAS Information Centre produces a range of factsheets which can be
requested directly or downloaded from the website
(www.oneworld.org/autism_uk/factsheet/factsh.html).

Autistic spectrum disorders
Statistics - how many people have autistic spectrum disorders?
Autism: a selective guide to books and videos
Asperger syndrome: a selective guide to books, articles and newsletters
Help for partners of people with Asperger syndrome
Handout for people with high functioning autism/Asperger individuals
Adolescents and adults with autism: a selective guide to resources
Semantic Pragmatic Impairments

Diagnosis
Autistic spectrum disorders: an aid to diagnosis (extract from Lorna Wing's
booklet)
The Centre for Social and Communication Disorders

Finance
Claiming Disability Living Allowance (DLA)
Financial provision by way of settlement or will for people with autism
Financial help: a parent's guide

Services
Care services for people with autism
Holiday help: a guide
Resource list on the education of children with autism
Resource list on Education Legislation (England & Wales)
Resource list on Education Legislation (Scotland)
List of National Autistic Society & local autistic society schools and
Resource list on adolescents and adults with autism
List of National Autistic Society & local autistic society adult centres and
Information sheet on the Accreditation Programme

Careers and courses
Opportunities for a career with the National Autistic Society

General
Perspective on a puzzle piece (history of the NAS)
Factsheet on the National Autistic Society
Information sheet for students
Membership form to join The National Autistic Society
Flyer to subscribe to Asperger United (newsletter specifically for people
with Asperger syndrome)
Flyer to subscribe to Titles in Autism (bulletin that lists research articles on
autism and related topics) and the Autism Research Database on CD-ROM.
Information pack on secretin
Vaccine information
Factsheet on Computer applications and people with autism

Approaches, therapies and interventions
SPELL approach
TEACCH approach
Daily Life Therapy: Higashi
LOVAAS method
Auditory Integration Training (AIT)
Facilitated Communication (FC)
Use of fictive symbols

Autism research database
The Autism Research Database is a computerised information resource
which has been developed over many years. The database currently stores

details of over 10,000 published books, articles and reports from across the world on autism and related subjects. In addition, information on professionals working in the autism field, research currently in progress, and details of forthcoming courses and conferences are included. The resources on the database are available in a number of ways:

Reference lists
The NAS Information Centre can carry out searches of the database and produce customised reference lists on any area of autism.

CD
The whole database is available as a read-only version on CD-ROM. The subscription fee (£95.00 + 17.5% VAT = £111.63) includes a copy of the whole of the database plus two updates.

Titles in Autism
New entries which are added to the database are included in the bulletin Titles in Autism. This bulletin, distributed three times a year, gives a full reference and summary abstract for each entry. Titles in Autism is divided into useful subject areas including diaganosis, assessment, biological perspectives, communication and therapies, approaches, behaviour management. An annual subscription costs £12.90 UK or £15.90 non-UK.

If you want to subscribe to any of the above services or would like any additional information please contact the NAS Information Centre, ☎ +44 (0)20 7903 3599, fax +44 (0)20 7903 3767, info@nas.org.uk.

Autism: the international journal of research and practice
Autism is a major new international forum for research of direct practical relevance to improving the quality of life for individuals with autism or autismrelated disorders.

Autism is co-published by Sage Publications and the NAS. Published four times a year the journal aims to encourage research into practice in the field of autism spectrum disorders, and encourage theoretical and academic researchers to consider the implications of their findings for practice. Articles include substantive research reports, as well as smaller-scale action research and case studies. Critical reviews of recent experimental work, and its relevance to intervention and care provision, are also a core feature of the journal.

If you would like to subscribe to the journal, an order form is available on the Sage website (www.sagepub.co.uk) or Sage Publications Ltd, 6 Bonhill Street, London EC2A 4PU (this address should also be used for all advertising enquiries). All NAS members can subscribe to *Autism* at a discounted rate.

Submissions details and the 'Notes to contributors' are available via the Sage website (www.sagepub.co.uk/journals/details/jo192.html) or from:

Submission Editor
Publications Department
The National Autistic Society
393 City Road
London EC1V 1NG
☎ 020 7903 3595
fax 020 7903 3767
autism@nas.org.uk

NAS Branches

The NAS has branches across the country, coordinated by the Development and Outreach Team. Please contact the Development Officer in your region for more details.

North East/North West
Luke Bearden
☎ 0115 911 3360

West Midlands
Chris Barson
☎ 0115 911 3360

Mid Counties
Alan Bicknell
☎ 0115 911 3368

Greater London
Greg Pasco
☎ 020 7903 3558

South East
Tracey Sellers
☎ 020 7903 3557

Gazeteer

South West
Jan Snook
☎ 0117 987 2575
Rachel Pike
☎ 0117 987 2575

Wales
Delyth Elward
☎ 01792 815915

Scotland
Gill West
☎ 0141 221 8090
Susan Chalmers

Northern Ireland
Jo Douglas, Project Officer
☎ 028 9027 4547

There are branches in in the following areas, but new ones are continually being set up:

Ayrshire
Barnet
Bath & NE Somerset
Brent
Bristol
Bromley
Buckinghamshire & Milton Keynes
Canterbury & Coastal Towns
Cheshire
Crewe and Nantwich
Cumbria
Devon
East Dunbartonshire
East Kent
Furness and South Cumbria
Greenwich
Guernsey
Harrow
Helensburgh & District
Hertfordshire
Humberside
Inverclyde

Jersey
Kingston
Lambeth
Newcastle
North Cumbria
North Lanarkshire
North Lincolnshire
North Somerset
North West Kent
North Yorkshire
Plymouth
Somerset
South Gloucestershire
South Kent
South Powys
Southwark
Stockport
Suffolk
Surrey
Torbay
West Dunbartonshire
Wiltshire

Societies affiliated to the NAS

All Lewisham Autism Support
22 Carholme Road
Forest Hill
London SE23 2HS
☎ 020 8291 9875
alas@bach.demon.co.uk

Asperger Syndrome Association of Ireland Ltd
85 Woodley Park
Kilmacud
Dublin 14
☎ 00 353 1 295 1389

Autism Bedfordshire
33 Fairford Avenue
Luton
Bedfordshire LU2 7ER
☎ 01582 724 117

Autistic Society for the Greater Manchester Area
25 Mulgrave Street
Swinton
Greater Manchester M27 9XH
☎ 0161 793 1323

Berkshire Autistic Society
Dyson Wood House
Tokem Green
Reading
Berkshire RG1 5BY

Bromley Autistic Trust
366b Crofton Road
Locksbottom
Orpington
Kent BR6 8NN
☎ 01689 857886

Cambridgeshire Autistic Society
1 Potton Road
Hilton
Cambridgeshire PE18 9NG
☎ 01480 830991

Children In Touch
45 Lower Road
Chinnor
Oxfordshire OX9 4DU
☎ 01844 351655

Children with Asperger Syndrome Support in East Lancashire
Pleasant View Farm
Goodshawfold
Rossendale
Lancashire BB4 8UF
☎ 01706 213605
rosalyn@cassel.k-web.co.uk

County Durham Autistic Support Group
PO Box 35
Spennymoor
County Durham DL16 6GL
☎ 01388 819880
cdasg@aol.com

Derbyshire Autistic Support Group
173 Nottingham Road
Alfreton
Derbyshire DE55 7FL
☎ 01773 835800

Devon & Cornwall Autistic Society
The Cottage
1 Old Pond Lane
Redruth
Cornwall TR15 1DN
☎ 01209 218584
s-wills@dcas.freeserve.co.uk

Devon and Cornwall Autistic Community Trust
Trafalgar House
Malpas Road
Truro
Cornwall TR1 1QH
☎ 01872 279198
mailbox@dcact.org

East Anglian Autistic Support Trust
52 Windsor Road
Cambridge
Cambridgeshire CB4 3JN
☎ 01223 358446
spencer_thomas@dial.pipex.com

Edinburgh Autistic Playschemes
18/6 Northfield Drive
Edinburgh
Lothian EH8 7RP
☎ 0131 538 4661

Essex Autistic Society
12 St Peters Court
St Peters Street
Colchester
Essex CO1 1WJ
☎ 01206 577678

European Services for People with Autism
South Hill College
9 The Cedars
Sunderland
Tyne & Wear SR2 7TW
☎ 0191 567 3523

Gloucestershire Group Homes
GGH, Springmill Business Centre
Avening Road
Nailsworth
Gloucestershire GL6 0BS
☎ 01453 835023
jackie@glos-grouphomes.demon.co.uk

Gwent Autistic Society
105 Allt-Yr-Yn Avenue
Newport
South Wales NP9 5DE
☎ 01633 263885

Hampshire Autistic Society
1634 Parkway
Solent Business Park
Fareham
Hampshire PO15 7AH
☎ 01489 880881
hautsoc@interalpha.co.uk

Help for Able Autistic Adults
42 Parkhill Road
Bexley
Kent DA5 1HU
☎ 01322 524681

Hertfordshire Autistic Community Trust
Queen Mother Resource Centre
Station Road
Bricket Wood
Hertfordshire AL2 3PJ
☎ 01923 678523

Highland Autistic Playschemes Initiative
Cullaird
Brackla
Cawdor
Nairn IV12 5QY

Highlands & Islands Autism Society
Aundorach
Nethybridge
Nethybridge
Highland PH25 3EF
☎ 01479 831274

Hill Park Housing Association
11a Pembury Road
Bexleyheath
Kent DA7 5LW
☎ 0181 319 5783

Hillingdon Autistic Care and Support
c/o Hillingdon Manor School
Moorcroft Complex
Harlington Road
Hillingdon
London UB8 3HD
☎ 020 8561 6039

The Huddersfield Support Group for Autism
4 Epson Way
Huddersfield
West Yorkshire HD5 0LE
☎ 01484 530 534

Isle of Man Support Group
Rydall
Brookfield Crescent
Ramsey
Isle of Man IM8 2JG
☎ 01624 813983

Isle of Wight Autistic Society
33 Manor Road
Lake
Isle of Wight PO36 9JA
☎ 01983 408721
sammy@gearing10.freeserve.co.uk

Kent Autistic Trust
14 High Street
Brompton
Kent ME7 5AE
☎ 01634 405168
brunning@kentautistic.demon.co.uk

Leeds & District Autism, Behaviour & Communication Support Group
72 Holtdale Park
Holt Park
Leeds
West Yorkshire LS16 7SJ
☎ 0113 226 3541

Leeds Christian Home for Adults with Autism
76 Potternewton Lane
Leeds
West Yorkshire LS7 3LW
☎ 0113 226 2700

Leicestershire Autistic Society
314 Hinckley Road
Leicester
Leicestershire LE3 0TN
☎ 0116 291 6958

Leisure for Autism
Anglo House
Chapel Road
Northenden
Manchester M22 4JN
☎ 0161 945 1070
leisureforautism@pop3.poptel.org.uk

Lincolnshire Autistic Society
21 Mill Lane
Donington
Spalding
Lincolnshire PE11 4TL
☎ 01775 821213
sibsey.staff@lrac.org.uk

Norfolk Autistic Community Housing Association Ltd
NACHA
49 Norwich Road
Dereham
Norfolk NR20 3AS
☎ 01362 698762

Gazeteer

Norfolk Autistic Society
Charing Cross Centre
17-19 St John Maddermarket
Norwich
Norfolk NR2 1DN
☎ 01603 631171

North Eastern Autistic Society
29 Graygarth Road
Berwick Hills
Middlesborough
Cleveland TS3 7QE
NEAS@galliford.freeserve.co.uk

North Wales Autistic Society
PO Box 1239
Conwy
Gwynedd LL31 9ZE
☎ 01492 545666

Northamptonshire Society for Autism
Suite 35 Burlington House
369 Wellingborough Road
Northampton
Northamptonshire NN1 4ET
☎ 01604 239404
norsocaut@compuserve.com

Nottingham Regional Society for Autistic Children and Adults
348a Carlton Hill
Nottingham
Nottinghamshire NG4 1JB
☎ 0115 987 3655
central-
services@norsaca.freeserve.co.uk

Oxfordshire Autistic Society for Information & Support
7 Mileway Gardens
Headington
Oxfordshire OX3 7XH
☎ 01865 750160

Parents and Professionals and Autism
Graham House
Knockbracken Healthcare Park
Belfast
Co. Down BT8 8BH
☎ 01232 401729

Perth Action on Autism
South Kinkell Farmhouse
Auchterarder
Perthshire

Renfrewshire Autism & Asperger Group
Garthdee
1 Millbrae
Bridge of Weir
Renfrewshire PA11 3LD
☎ 01505 614566

Sheffield Autistic Society
78 Well Green Road
Stannington
Sheffield
South Yorkshire S6 6DF
☎ 0114 285 4770
joanne@darwin78.freeserve.co.uk

South & Mid Glamorgan Autistic Society
52 Woodland Avenue
Pencoed
Mid Glamorgan CF35 6UP
☎ 01656 861302

Strathclyde Autistic Society
7th Floor, Fleming House
134 Renfrewshire Street
Glasgow G3 6ST
☎ 0141 331 0223

Stroud Court Community Centre
Stroud Court, Longfords
Minchinhampton
Gloucester
Gloucestershire GL6 9AN
☎ 01453 834020
stroudcourt@compuserve.com

Surrey Autistic Community Trust (The)
22 The Ridgeway
Fetcham
Surrey KT22 9AZ
☎ 01372 372807

Sussex Autistic Society
Bridge House
40 Keymer Road
Hassocks
West Sussex BN6 8AP
☎ 01273 846846
june@sussexautistic.freeserve.co.uk

Thorne House Services for Autism Ltd
Thorne House
St Nicholas Road
Thorne, Doncaster
South Yorkshire DN8 5BG
☎ 01405 812128

Tyne & Wear Autistic Society
21 Thornhill Park
Sunderland
Tyne & Wear
SR2 7LA
☎ 0191 561 1994

Wargrave House School
449 Wargrave Road
Newton Le Willows
Merseyside WA12 8RS
☎ 01925 224 899

Wessex Autistic Society
51 Bargates
Christchurch
Dorset BH23 1QD
☎ 01202 483360
twas@talk21.com

West Midlands Autistic Society Ltd
17b Fellows Lane
Harborne
Birmingham
West Midlands B17 9TS
☎ 0121 426 4225
wmas.org@virgin.net

Wirral Autistic Society
72 Manor Drive
Upton
Merseyside L49 6LQ
☎ 0151 677 4328
keith@neilhouse.demon.co.uk

Gazeteer

Schools
(in alphabetical order)

Broomhayes School
Kingsley House
Alverdiscott Road
Bideford
North Devon EX39 4PL
☎ 01237 473830
(NAS school)

**Camphill Rudolf Steiner
Schools**
Camphill Medical Centre
Murtle Estate
Bieldside
Aberdeen
AB1 9EP
☎ 01224 867935

The Children's Service
104 Broadway
Derby
DE22 1BP
☎ 01332 347592
(Community Health Services
NHS Trust, Southern Derbyshire)

Church Hill School
(independent)
The Old Rectory
Church Hill
Banham
Norfolk
NR16 2HN
☎ 01953 887815

Daldorch House School
Sorn Road
Catrine
East Ayrshire KA5 6NA
☎ 01290 551666
(NAS school)

Doucecroft School
163 High St
Kelvedon
Colchester
Essex CO5 9JA
☎ 01376 570060
(Essex Autistic Society)

Green Hedges School
Bar Lane
Stapleford
Cambridge
CB2 5BJ
☎ 01223 508608
(Cambridgeshire County Council)

The Hayward School
Autism Resource Base
Maltese Road
Chelmsford
Essex CM1 2PA
☎ 01245 258667
(Essex Education Authority)

The Helen Allison School
Longfield Road
Meopham
Kent
DA13 0EW
☎ 01474 814878
(NAS school)

Hope Lodge School
22 Midanbury Lane
Bitterne Park
Southampton SO18 4HP
☎ 01703 634346
(Hampshire Autistic Society)

Inscape House School
Schools Hill
Cheadle
Cheshire SK8 1JE
☎ 0161 283 4750
(Boys and Girls Welfare Society)

Lidgett Grove School
Wheatlands Grove
Acomb
York   YO26 5NH
☎ 01904 791437
(City of York Educational
Services)

The Loddon School
(independent)
Sherfield on Loddon
Hook
Hampshire RG27 0JD
☎ 01256 882394

Kisharon Schools
Kisharon Day School
(Junior)
1011 Finchley Road
London
NW11 7HB
☎ 0181 455 7483
(Kisharon Autistic Services)

Kisharon Autistic Services
(Senior Centre 16+)
37 Moss Hall Grove
London N12 8PE
☎ 0181 343 9174
(Senior Centre 16+)

Peterhouse School
Preston New Road
Southport PR9 8PA
☎ 01704 506682
(Autism Initiatives)

Portfield School
4 Magdalen Lane
Christchurch
Dorset   BH23 1PH
☎ 01202 486626
(Wessex Autistic Society school)

Prior's Court School
Hermitage
Thatcham
Berkshire
RG18 9NU
☎ 01635 247 202
(Higashi Hope Foundation)

Radlett Lodge School
Harper Lane
Radlett
Hertfordshire WD7 9HW
☎ 01923 854922
(NAS school)

Robert Ogden School
(formerly Storm School)
Clayton Lane
Thurnscoe
Rotherham
South Yorkshire
S63 0BE
☎ 01709 874443
(NAS school)

Rowan Lodge
Oaklands Park School Autism
Unit
John Nash Drive
Dawlish
Devon EX7 9SF
☎ 01626 862363
(Devon County Education
Authority)

Struan House School
27 Claremont,
Alloa
Clackmannanshire FK10 2DF
☎ 01259 213435
(Scottish Society for Autistism)

Sutherland House Schools
(Nottingham Regional Society
for Autistic Children and
Adults)
Early Years Centre
272 Longdale Lane
Ravenshead
Nottingham NG15 9AH
☎ 01623 490879
Sutherland House
(primary)
Sutherland Road
Nottingham NG3 7AP
☎ 0115 987 3375
Sutherland House
(secondary)
Westward
68 Cyprus Road
Mapperley Park
Nottingham NG3 5ED
☎ 0115 969 1823
Continuing Education Centre
8 Clinton Avenue
Nottingham
N95 1AW
☎ 0115 696 3373

The Sybil Elgar School
Havelock Road
Southall
Middlesex UB2 4NZ
☎ 020 8813 9168
(NAS school)

Thornhill Park School
21 Thornhill Park
Sunderland
SR2 7LA
☎ 0191 514 0659
(Tyne & Wear Autistic Society)

Treehouse
49 Meckleburgh Square
London
WC1N 2NY
☎ 0120 7681 9982
(The Treehouse Trust)

Wargrave House School
449 Wargrave Road
Newton-le-Willows
Merseyside WA12 8RS
☎ 01925 224899
(Wargrave House Limited)

Ysgol Plas Brondyffryn
Ystrad Road
Denbigh LL16 4RH
☎ 01745 813841
(Denbighshire County Council)

Adult centres

NAS services
Further details on NAS establishments can be obtained from Director of Services, The National Autistic Society, Church House, Church Road, Filton, Bristol BS34 7BD
☎ 0117 987 2575.

Most of the services listed are active participants in the NAS Accreditation Programme (denoted 'Accredited'). For detailed information on accreditation status please contact the individual services direct or
NAS Accreditation Programme Manager
236 Henleaze Road
Bristol BS9 4NG
UK
☎ 0117 962 8962
fax 0117 962 2220

Burnham Service
Park View
1 Westfield Road
Burnham-on-Sea
Somerset TA8 2AW
☎ 01278 792 962/789 888
fax 01278 795 961
Burnham@nas.org.uk
Accredited

Cambridgeshire Service
Juniper House
High Street
Stretham
Ely
Cambridge CB6 3LD
☎ 01353 648 797
fax 01353 648 712
Cambridgeshire@nas.org.uk

Croydon Service
6 St Edwards Close
New Addington
Croydon
Surrey CR0 0EL
☎ 01689 800 960
fax 01689 800 861
Croydon@nas.org.uk
Accredited

Gravesend Service
Overcliffe House
SAND
22-24 Princes Street
Gravesend
Kent DA11 0DN
☎ 01474 535 057
fax 01474 564 259
Gravesend@nas.org.uk
Accredited

The Hayes Unit
Rookery Lane
Pilning Bristol
Avon BS35 4JN
☎ 01454 632 311
fax 01454 633 031
Hayes@nas.org.uk

Hyndburn Service
Margaret House
Queen Street
Great Harwood
Blackburn
Lancashire BB6 7QP
☎ 01254 888 535
fax 01254 876 837
Hyndburn@nas.org.uk
Accredited

The LEAP Service
Acton Centre
The Woodlands Building
Mill Hill Road
Acton
London W3 8UX
☎ 020 8992 6611
fax 020 8992 6644
West.London@nas.org.uk
Accredited

Leicester Service
Grovebrook House
Brook Street
Whetstone
Leicestershire LE8 6LA
☎ 0116 286 6956
fax 0116 275 2217
Leicester@nas.org.uk

Manchester Service
Anglo House
Chapel Road
Northenden
Manchester M23 9EW
☎ 0161 945 0040
fax 0161 945 3038
Manchester@nas.org.uk

Mildenhall Service
Middlefield Manor
The Street
Barton Mills
nr Bury St Edmunds
Suffolk IP28 6AW
☎ 01638 716 910
fax 01638 510 925
Mildenhall@nas.org.uk
Accredited

Neath Service
Longford Court
Longford
Neath SA10 7HN
☎ 01792 814611
fax 01792 321609
Neath@nas.org.uk

Newport Service
Orchard House
11a Norman Street
Caerleon, Newport
South Wales NP18 1BB
☎ 01633 423 537
fax 01633 430 701
Newport@nas.org.uk
Accredited

Northamptonshire Service
Leyland Resource Centre
56 Leyland Trading Estate
Irthlingborough Road
Wellingborough
Northamptonshire NN8 1RS
☎ 01933 440 910
fax 01933 440 915
Northamptonshire@nas.org.uk

Somerset Court
Harp Road
Brent Knoll
Somerset TA9 4HQ
☎ 01278 760 555
Fax 01278 760 747
Somerset.Court@nas.org.uk
Accredited

Surrey Service
42-44 Stonepit Close
Godalming
Surrey GU7 2LS
☎ 01483 861 066
fax 01483 861 055
Surrey@nas.org.uk

West London Service
57 Halliday Square
Southall
Middlesex UB1 3EU
☎ 020 8813 8222
fax 020 8813 8228
Accredited

Other services

Many local groups/organisations run more than one unit or have 'split -site' establishments providing residential accommodation and/or day facilities. Please contact the services direct for further information.

Adult Development Service
Anglesey Lodge
Anglesey Road
Gosport
Hampshire PO12 2DX
☎ 023 9252 4243
fax 023 9258 9965
hasads@interalpha.co.uk
(Hampshire Autistic Society)
Accredited

Ashlar House
76 Potternewton Lane
Leeds
West Yorkshire LS7 3LW
☎ 0113 226 2700
fax 0113 226 2700
(Leeds Christian Home for Adults with Autism)
Accredited

Ashleigh College
3 Elmfield Park
Gosforth
Newcastle-upon-Tyne NE3 4UX
☎ 0191 213 0833
fax 0191 213 2614
(European Services for People with Autism)
Accredited

Balmyre House
Whins Road
Alloa
Clackmannanshire FK10 3RH
☎ 01259 218 433
fax 01259 720 062
(Scottish Society for Autistic Children)
Accredited

Burton Cottages
Bishops Lane
Robertsbridge
East Sussex TN32 5BA
☎ 01580 881 715
fax 01580 881 715
(Sussex Autistic Society)
Accredited

Clannalba House
Lamington
Nr. Biggar
ML12 6HP
☎ 01899 850 633
fax 01899 850 330
(Scottish Society for Autistic Children)

Dyson's Wood House
Dyson's Wood
Tokers Green
Reading
Berkshire RG4 9EY
☎ 0118 972 4553
fax 0118 972 3479
(The Disabilities Trust)
Accredited

Fife Unit Adult Services
Unit 34
Thistle Industrial Estate,
Church Street
Cowdenbeath
Fife KY4 8LP
☎ 01383 610 754
fax 01383 611 926
(Scottish Society for Autistic
Children)
Accredited

Gloucester Group Homes
Spring Mill Business Centre
Avening Road
Nailsworth
Gloucestershire GL6 0BU
☎ 01453 835 023
fax 01453 836 932
(Gloucestershire Group Homes
Trust)
Accredited

Gorse Farm
Coleshill Road,
Marston Green
Birmingham B37 7HP
☎ 0121 770 9085
fax 0121 770 9647
wmas@virgin.net
(West Midlands Autistic Society)

High Croft
Whetley Road
Broadwindsor
Beaminster
Dorset DT8 3QT
☎ 01308 868 360 or 01460 77033
(office hours)
fax 01308 867 680
(Wessex Autistic Society)
Accredited

Hillside View
160 Whitehouse Lane
Walkley
Sheffield S6 2UZ
☎ 0114 231 6770
fax 0114 231 6770
(Thorne House Services for
Autism)

Kent Autistic Trust
14 High Street
Brompton
Gilllingham
Kent ME7 5AE
☎ 01634 405 168
Fax 01634 811 282
(Kent Autistic Trust)
Accredited

Lambert House
36 Notridge Road
Bowthorpe
Norwich
Norfolk NR5 9BE
☎ 01603 749 845
fax 01603 749 460
(Norfolk Autistic Community
Housing Association Ltd)
Accredited

Mid/East Lothian Adult Services
21b North High Street
Musselburgh
East Lothian EH21 6JA
☎ 0131 665 6659
fax 0131 665 4300
(Scottish Society for Autistic
Children)

Nicholas House
Cairns Close
St Albans
Hertfordshire AL4 0EY
☎ 01727 839 909
fax 01727 839 909
nshellard@tinyonline.co.uk
(Hertfordshire Autistic Society)

Oakfield House
6-12 Oakfield Road
Selly Park
Birmingham B29 7EJ
☎ 0121 471 1913
fax 0121 414 0017
(West Midlands Autistic Society)
Accredited

Peldon Old Rectory
Church Road
Peldon, Colchester
Essex CO5 7PT
☎ 01206 735 206/735 279
fax 01206 735 206
(Essex Autistic Society)
Accredited

**Queen Elizabeth The Queen
Mother Centre**
Station Road,
Bricket Wood, St. Albans
Hertfordshire AL2 3PJ
☎ 01923 678 523
fax 01923 893 467
(Hertfordshire Autistic Community
Trust)
Accredited

Raby Hall
Raby Hall Road
Bromborough
Wirral L63 ONN
☎ 0151 334 7510
fax 0151 334 1762
MikeHatton@RabyHall.demon.co.uk
(Wirral Autistic Society)
Accredited

Ravenswood
34 Ilkeston Road
Heanor
Derbyshire DE75 7DT
☎ 01773 769 278
fax 01773 769 278
(Nottingham Regional Society for
Autistic Children & Adults)
Accredited

Ridgepark House
Mousebank Road
Lanark ML11 7RA
☎ 01555 665 988
fax 01555 666 731
(Scottish Society for Autistic
Children)
Accredited

Seaham Community
9 The Cedars
Ashbrooke
Sunderland SR2 7TW
☎ 0191 567 3523
fax 0191 514 3858
espashill@btinternet.com
(European Services for People with
Autism)
Accredited

Gazeteer

South Hill College
9 The Cedars
Ashbrooke
Sunderland SR2 7TW
☎ 0191 567 3523
fax 0191 514 3858
espashill@btinternet.com
(European Services for People with
Autism)
Accredited

Stroud Court
Longfords
Minchinhampton
Gloucestershire GL6 9AN
☎ 01453 834 020
fax 01453 837 220
(Stroud Court Community Trust)
Accredited

Sutherland House School
Continuing Education Centre,
8 Clinton Avenue
Nottingham NG5 1AW
☎ 0115 969 3373
fax 0115 985 8911
cec@sutherlandhouse.org.uk
(Nottingham Regional Society for
Autistic Children & Adults)
Accredited

Thornbeck College
14 Thornhill Park
Sunderland SR2 7LA
☎ 0191 510 2038
fax 0191 514 3684
(Tyne & Wear Autistic Society)
Accredited

Thorne House
St. Nicholas Road
Thorne, Doncaster
South Yorkshire DN8 5BG
☎ 01405 812 128
fax 01405 741 081
(Thorne House Services for Autism)
Accredited

Trafalgar House
Malpas Road
Truro
Cornwall
TR1 1QH
☎ 01872 279198
fax 01872 262009

Upper Ford Lodge
Ford Lane
Droitwich Spa
Worcestershire WR9 0BQ
☎ 01905 779 949
fax 01905 779 245
kevin@upperfordlodge.freeserve.co.uk
(West Midlands Autistic Society)

Whitegates
Sparken Hill
Worksop
Nottinghamshire S80 1AP
☎ 01909 478 746
fax 01909 475 162
(Nottingham Regional Society for
Autistic Children & Adults)
Accredited

Whitstone
49 Norwich Road
Dereham
Norfolk NR20 3AS
☎ 01362 698762
fax 01362 699792
(Norfolk Autistic Community
Housing Association Ltd)
Accredited

Other services that accept people with an autistic spectrum disorder

Charities

63a Alfredston Place
Wantage
Oxon OX12 8DL
☎ 01235 772 551
fax 01235 772 551
(United Response UK)

Ardcora
Ardglass Road
Downpatrick
Co. Down
Northern Ireland BT30 6RA
☎ 028 9061 7110
Fax 028 9061 7814
(Downe Residential Project)

Conchiglia
Thrupp Lane
Radley
Nr Abingdon
Oxon OX14 3NG
☎ 01235 550 978
fax 01235 550 978
(The Kingwood Trust)
Accredited

Cornfields/Cornview
124 Roman Road
Winklebury
Basingstoke
Hants RG23 8HF
☎ 01256 350 827
fax 01256 350 827
cathie@cornview.demon.co.uk
(Liaise Loddon Ltd.)

Frank House
8a Twigg Close
Erith
Kent DA8 3LD
☎ 01322 334 318
fax: 01322 334 318
(Hill Park Housing Association Ltd)
Accredited

Hamilton House
10 Crescent Road
Bromley BR1 3PW
☎ 01689 857 886
fax 01689 860 485
(Bromley Autistic Trust)
Accredited

Hucklow Road
19-21 Hucklow Road
Firth Park
Sheffield S5 6TB
☎ 0114 261 0918
fax 0114 261 0918
(Mencap)

Hudson Way
Isabella Court
72a Westgate
Pickering
North Yorkshire YO18 8AU
☎ 01751 474 740
(The Wilf Ward Family Trust)

Marriott Road
18 Marriott Road
Barnet
Hertfordshire EN5 4NJ
☎ 020 8449 9493
fax 020 8449 9493
(Hoffman de Visme Foundation)

Gazeteer

Stanmore/Endymion Project
Stanmore Road
40 Stanmore Road
London N5 3SP
☎ 020 8889 6041
Endymion Road
2 Endymion Road
London N4 1EE
☎ 020 8341 3888
fax 020 8341 3888
(Hoffman de Visme Foundation)

Privately owned

Access House
9-11 Knollbeck Crescent,
Brampton
Barnsley S73 0TT
☎ 01226 756 522
fax 01226 756 522
(Mike Kruszynski/Kath Knox)

Agnes House
79 Newbury Lane
Oldbury
Warley B69 1HE
☎ 0121 552 5141
Fax 0121 552 5141
(Alphonsus Homes)

Alderson Road
12 Alderson Road
Harrogate
North Yorkshire HG2 8AS
☎ 01423 520 251
fax 01937 587 729
(Northern Life Care)
Accredited

Ashfield Court
Stoneyford Road
Sutton-in-Ashfield
Nottinghamshire NG17 2DR
☎ 01623 512 666
fax 01623 559 9166
(Trinity Care plc)

Avalon House
3 King Street
Cheltenham
Gloucestershire GL50 4AU
☎ 01242 582 559
(Advances in Autism Care &
Education)

Bangeston Hall
London Road
Pembroke Dock
Pembrokeshire SA72 4RX
☎ 01646 683 173
fax 01646 681 996
(Pembrokeshire Resource Centre)
Accredited

Bangor
People's Park Road
Crediton
Devon EX17 2DA
☎ 01363 772 215/773 291
Fax 01363 775 822
(Crediton Care & Support Homes)

Binnegar Hall
(Purbeck Court Autism Unit)
East Stoke
Wareham
Dorset BH20 6AT
☎ 01929 552 201
fax 01929 552 201
(Krystal Health Care)

Chippings
28 Russells Crescent
Horley
Surrey RH6 7DN
☎ 01293 775 350
fax 01737 218 691
(Gresham Care)

Cloverdale House
Abbotsford Grove
Thornholme Road
Thornhill
Sunderland SR7 2JS
☎ 0191 565 7070
fax 0191 557 7400
(Covertaste Ltd.)

Gammaton Nursery
Gammaton Cross
East of the Water
Bideford
North Devon EX39 4QE
☎ 01237 474 853
Fax 01237 474 853
simon.trow42@freeserve.co.uk
(Satinclose Care Ltd)

Ganwick House
Wagon Road
Barnet
Hertfordshire EN4 0PH
☎ 020 8447 1155
Fax 020 8447 1166
(Brookdale Healthcare)

Gloucestershire Autism Services
87 Bouncers Lane
Prestbury
Cheltenham
Gloucestershire GL52 5JB
☎ 01242 572 446
fax 01242 572 446
(Gloucestershire Autism Services)

Healthlinc House
Cliff Road
Welton
Lincoln LN2 3JN
☎ 01673 862 000
fax 01673 862 000
(Healthlinc House)

Heath Farm
Heath Road
Scopwick
Sleaford
Lincolnshire LN4 3JD
☎ 01526 320 312
fax 01526 323 071
heath.farm@btinternet.com;
www.btinternet.com/~stephen.henton
(Lincolnshire Care Services)
Accredited

The InterACT Centre
Hanwell Community Centre
Westcott Crescent
Hanwell
London W7 1PD
☎ 020 8575 0046
Fax 020 8575 0046
jamesg@dircon.co.uk
(The InterACT Centre)
Accredited

Kelsey Care
1 Old Bexley Lane
Bexley
Kent DA5 2DY
☎ 01322 621 400
fax 01322 621 444
(Kelsey Care)

The Lodge
18 Huntspill Road
Highbridge
Somerset TA8 3DQ
☎ 01278 786 618
(RJ Holmes)

Maesteilo Care Home
Capel Isaac
Llandeilo
Carmarthenshire SA19 7TG
☎ 01558 668 510
fax 01558 668 906
(Maesteilo Care Home)

26 Mills Road
Devonport
Plymouth
PL1 4NF
☎ 01752 204 598
(Trillium Care Ltd)

Four Nevill Park
Tunbridge Wells
Kent TN4 8NW
☎ 01892 519 520
fax 01892 536 766
Nevill@angevin.btinternet.com
(Angevin Limited)

30 Norbury Crescent
Norbury
London SW16 4LA
☎ 020 8765 0431
Fax 020 8765 0431
(Norcrest Homes Ltd)

Norfolk Lodge
9 Norfolk Road
Horsham
West Sussex RH12 1BZ
☎ 01403 218 876
fax 01403 218 876
(Sussex Health Care)

The Old Rectory
27 Stallard Street
Trowbridge
Wiltshire BA14 9AA
☎ 01225 777 728
(Satinclose Care Ltd)

12 Park Road
Soughborough
Tunbridge Wells
Kent
TN4 0NX
☎ 01892 616600
fax 01892 617013
(Angevin Ltd)

Pelicans Further Education College
St. Mary's Road
Meare
Glastonbury
Somerset BA6 9SP
☎ 01458 860 536
fax 01458 860 536
staff@pelicans- college.demon.co.uk
(Pelicans Further Education College)

Robleaze House
539 Bath Road
Brislington
Bristol BS4 3LB
☎ 0117 972 0813
(Mr & Mrs A J Robinson)

Rogerstone House
73 Risca Road
Rogerstone
Newport
Gwent NP10 9GD
☎ 01633 614 365
(CCA Residential Homes Ltd)

Spring Lake
17 Forty Lane
Wembley Park
Middlesex HA9 9EU
☎ 020 8908 5233/8908 5444
fax 020 8908 5233
(Waterhouse Ltd)

The Springs Community
Coast Drive
St. Mary's Bay
Kent TN29 0HN
☎ 01797 363 550
fax 01797 361 040
(The Springs Community Ltd)

St Marks
23 Collier Road
West Hill
Hastings TN34 3JR
☎ 01424 200 854/431 686
fax 01424 200 854
(Mr & Mrs Dominic Kennard)

Tower House
34 Higher Brimley Road
Teignmouth
Devon TQ14 8JU
☎ 01626 776 515
fax 01626 776 611
(South Devon Autism Resource
Centre Ltd)
Accredited

Wood Dene
Colliery Approach
Outwood
Wakefield WF3 3JH
☎ 01924 825252
fax 01924-835543
admin@wooddene.enterprise-
plc.com
(Life Links Ltd)
Accredited

Woodend
Cannongate
Hythe
Kent CT21 5PX
☎ 01303 230 131
fax 01303 230 131
info@lothlorien.co.uk
(The Lothlorien Community
Limited)

Wycar Leys House
Kirklington Road
Old Bilsthorpe
Nottingham NG22 8TT
☎ 01623 871 752
fax 01623 871 118
(Wycar Leys House)

Health Trusts

Ashmount
St Ebbas Hospital,
Hook Road
Epsom
Surrey KT19 8QJ
☎ 01372 20 20 20
(Surrey Oaklands NHS Trust)

Autism Day Service
Leicester Frith Hospital
Groby Road
Leicester LE3 9QF
☎ 0116 256 3263
fax 0116 231 4810
(Leicestershire & Rutland Health
Care NHS Trust)
Accredited

Jupiter Autism Specific Services
(JASS)
Gallwey Unit
St Ebbas Hospital
Hook Road, Epsom
Surrey KT19 8QJ
☎ 01372 203 185
fax 01372 203 214
gallwey@demon.co.uk
(Surrey Oaklands NHS Trust)

Maple House
4 Hospital Lane
Whipton
Exeter EX1 3PQ
☎ 01392 208 390
fax 01392 208 391
(Exeter & East Devon Community
Health Service Trust)

Gazeteer

6 Meadow Close
Harperbury Hospital
Harper Lane
Shenley, Radlett
Hertfordshire WD7 9HQ
☎ 01923 427 276
(Horizon NHS Trust)

Oak House
Aston Hall
Aston-on-Trent
Derby DE72 2AL
☎ 01332 792 412 ext 256
fax 01332 792 039
(Community Health Services NHS
Trust Southern Derbyshire)

The Sunderland Service
11 Serlby Close
Coach Road
High Usworth
Washington
Tyne & Wear NE37 1EN
☎ 0191 415 5041
fax 0191 514 5041
28 Hylton Bank
South Hylton
Sunderland
Tyne & Wear
NE37 1EN
☎ 0191 415 5041
fax 0191 514 5041
(Northgate & Prudhoe NHS Trust)

South Lodge Group Home
St Ebba's Hospital
Hook Road
Epsom KT19 8QJ
☎ 01372 203 029
fax 01372 203 103
(Surrey Oaklands NHS Trust)
Accredited

Woodside Villa
Northgate Hospital
Morpeth
Northumberland NE61 3BP
☎ 01670 394 116
fax 01670 394 002
(Northgate & Prudhoe NHS Trust)
Accredited

Local Authorities

Burnside
1 Burnside
Eastfield
Scarborough YO11 3LH
☎ 01723 583 802
(North Yorkshire County Council
Social Services Directorate)

Day Options Development
Stonebridge Day Centre
Twybridge Way
Hillside
London NW10 0SL
☎ 020 8961 4489
fax 020 8961 0355
(Brent Social Services)

Starbeck
80 High Street
Starbeck
Harrogate HG2 7LW
☎ 01423 883 301
fax 01423 887 550
(North Yorkshire County Council
Social Services Directorate)

Westminster Day Service
133 Droop Street
London W10 4DB
☎ 020 7641 5852
fax 020 7641 5857
(Westminster Day & Employment
Services)

International societies and associations

Autism Europe
The International Association
Autism Europe
Rue E. Van Becelaere 26 B,
Bte 21
B - 1170 Bruxelles
Belgium
☎ +32 0 2 675 7505
fax +32 0 2 675 7270

(* Member Associations: Autisme
Europe = 38)

Argentina
Centro de Atencion Integral Para
Ninos Autista y Psicoticos
Santiago Del Estero 239
4400 Salta Argentina
☎ +54 87 211326

Australia
Autism Victoria
P.O. Box 235
Ashburton
Victoria 3147
Australia
☎ +61 3 98 85 0533
fax +61 3 98 85 0508
autismav@vicnet.net.au

Autism Association Queensland
P.O. Box 363
437 Hellawell Road
Sunnybank Hills
Queensland 4109
Australia
☎ +61 0 73 273 2222
www.autismqld.asn.au

Association for Autistic Children in
Western Australia
Suite 114
396, Scarborough Beach Road
Osborne Park
Western Australia 6017

Autism Tasmania
PO Box 1552
Launceston
TAS 7250
Australia
☎ +61 0 03 43 2308
fax +61 0 03 43 2308

Autism Association of South
Australia Inc
PO Box 339
Fullerton
South Australia 5062
Australia
☎ +61 0 88 379 6976
fax +61 0 88 338 1216
aasa@adelaide.on.net

Autistic Association of New South
Wales
PO Box 361
Forestville
NSW 2087, Australia
☎ +61 (0) 29 452 5088
fax: +61 (0) 29 451 3447
aanswnet@ozemail.com.au

Austria
Österreichische Austistenhilfe
Esslinggasse 13/3/11
A - 1010 Wien
Austria
☎ +43 1 533 9666
fax +43 1 533 7847

Bangladesh
Training and Education for Autistic
Children
GPO Box 338
Dhaka - 1000
Bangladesh
☎/fax +8 02 912 8791
teach@bdcom.com

Belgium
Association de Parents pour
L'epanouissement des
Personnes Autistes*
Rue Château des Balances, 3 bte
27
5000 Namur
Belgium
☎/fax +32 81 744350
stephanie.charpentier@ping.be

Vlaamse Vereniging Autisme*
Contact:
Groot Begijnhof, 14
B - 9040 Gent
Belgium
☎ +32 078 152 252
fax +32 092 188 383
vva@autisme-vl.be

Bermuda
Bermuda Autism Support Group
Contact: Mrs Alison Dyer
PO Box HM 641
Hamilton
Bermuda
HMCV
☎ +1 809 441 292 1115
fax +1 809 441 295 7909
dyerp@hotmail.com

Brazil
Associacão Brasileira de Autismo
(Deuzina)
Sector de Divulgacao e Publicaoes
Estrada Da Canoa 401
S. Conrado (22610)

Rio de Janeiro
Brazil
☎ +55 0 61233 1337
AUTISMO@mrnet.com.br

Federaçào Paulista De Autismo -
FEPA
Casade Espereanca
Rua José Vilar
938 - Aldeota
CEP: 60.125-00
Brazil
☎ 55 0 85 224 0702
fax +55 085 261 6964

Bulgaria
Parent's Association Autistic Child
Sofia*
Medical Academy
Dept. of Child Psychiatry
33 Prochlada str.
BG - 1619 Sofia
Bulgaria
☎ +359 2 57 30 13

Canada
Autism Society Canada
PO Box 635
Frederiction
New Brunswick
E3B 5B4
☎ +1 506 363 8815

Chile
DNG Corporacion Andalue
Eulalia Monge de Barros
7 Norte 544
Vina del Mar
Chile
☎ +56 32 97 1523
jlbarros@entelchile.net

Colombia
Association of Parents with
Autistic Children
Transv. 29 # 118-32

Apartado Aereo No.40621
Santa Fe de Bogota D.C.
Colombia
☎ +57 1 620 3792

Croatia
Croatian Society for Helping
Autistic Persons*
Dvorniciceva 6
10000 Zagreb
Croatia
☎ +38 51 468 3867
fax +38 51 468 3867

Association for the Care of Autistic
Persons - Rijeka (Part of CSHAP)
Senjskih Usokoka 1
51000 Rijeka
Croatia
☎ +38 55 151 2344

Society for Autism - Split
Vukovarska 15
21000 Split
Croatia
☎ +38 52 158 9845

Czech Republic
Autistic
Kyselova 1189/24
182 00 Prague 8, Czech Republic
☎ +42 2 858 4141

Denmark
Landsforeningen Autisme
Skovvejen 48
DK - 8740 Braedstrup
Denmark
☎ +45 7575 2818
fax +45 7575 3818

Information & Research Centre for
Autism in Denmark
Skodsborgvej 1,3
DK-2830 Virum

Denmark
☎ +45 85 1213/85 2355
fax + 45 85 9313
videnscentre@vip.cybercity.dk

Egypt
The Egyptian Autistic Society
President: Dahlia Soliman
9 Road 215
Degla, Maadi
Cairo, Eygpt
☎ +20 2 519 9033
fax +20 2 519 7055
Email: dahlia@zeus.starnet.com.eg

Estonia
Estonian Autistic Society*
Rõõmu tee 18-1
Tartu, Estonia, 510133
☎ +372 27 339807

Finland
Finnish Association for Autism*
Laivurinrinne 2 A 2
SF-00120 Helsinki
Finland
☎ +358 0 63 66 20

France (see also Reunion Islands)
Association pour la Prise en
Charge dess Anomalies de
Development de
L'Enfant*
32 Boulevard de la Bastille
75012 Paris
France
☎ +331 4004 9000
fax +331 4004 9024

Autism - Ile de France*
52 Rue du Docteur Blanche
F - 75016 Paris
France
☎ +331 4525 8252

Association de Parents et de
Professionnels pour l'education,
le developpement, l'integration des
Personnes atteintes d'autisme*
2, rue Albert de Mun, bat. 3
F - 92190 Meudon
France
☎ +33 4623 0523

E.D.I. Formation*
15 Rue de la Terrasse
06110 Le Cannet
France
☎ +33 4 9345 5318
fax +33 4 9369 9047

Les Ateliers-Foyers de Valbonne
Association "La Bourguette, Le
Grand Réal, Valbonne"
Domaine de Valbonne
Route de Flassans
83 340 Cabasse
France
☎ +33 (0) 4 9469 6969
fax +33 (0) 4 9469 6970

Sesame Autisme FFAPI*
18 Rue Etex
75018 Paris
France
☎ +33 1 4228 5709
fax +33 1 4542 5648

Union Nationale des Associations
de Parents et Amis

de Personnes Handicapees
Mentales (UNAPEI)*
15 Rue Coysevox
75876 Paris Cedex 18
France
☎ +33 1 4485 5050
fax +33 1 4485 5060

Association Francaise Pour l'Aide
aux Autistes (AFPAA)
42 rue Benard
75014 Paris
France
☎ /fax +33 0 1 4541 5293
http://www.eleves.ens.fr:8080/hom
e/meltz/PAAOhtlm

Association Autisme France*
1, Place D'Aine
87000 Limoges
France
☎ +33 0 5537 0463
fax +33 5 5537 0467

Association Envol*
Bastide Collombe
83119 Brue Auriac
France
☎ +33 16 9480 9323
fax +33 4 9480 9315

Autisme Auvergne*
Mireille Lemahieu
4 Avenue Bergougnam
63400 Chamalieres
France
☎ +33 04 7328 7101
fax +33 04 7328 0913

Autisme Bourbonnais*
"La Prat" Route d'Hauterive
F - 03700 Bellerive S/Allier
France

Autisme Poitou-Charentes -
Partenaire Autism France*
Le Petit Chadignac
17100 Saintes
France
☎ +44 05 4 6993 0188

Association Autisme Loire
4 Rue Andre Malraux
42000 Saint Etienne
France
☎ +44 33 4 7773 3204

Germany
H.A.K Bundesverband Hilfe fur
das Autistische Kind*
Bebelalee 141
D-22297 Hambourg
Germany
☎ +49 40 511 5604
fax +49 40 511 0813

**Great Britain and Northern
Ireland**
The National Autistic Society*
393 City Road
London
England EC1V 1NG
☎ +44 0 20 7833 2299
fax +44 0 20 7833 9666
nas@nas.org.uk

Parents and Professionals and
Autism*
Knockbracken
Healthcare Park
Saintfield Road
Belfast BT8 8BH
Ireland
☎ +44 0 28 9040 1729
fax +44 0 28 9040 3467

Scottish Society for Autistism
Hilton House
Alloa Business Park
Whins Road
Alloa
Scotland, FK10 3SA
☎ +44 01259 720044

Greece
Greek Society for the Protection of
Autistic People*
c/o Prof. C. Alexiou
President
2 Athenas Street
GR - 10551 Athens
Greece
☎ +30 1 321 6550
fax +30 1 321 6549- Prof. Alexiou

Association of Parents and Friends
of the Autistic Child "ELPIDA"*
Contact: Elpida Grigoriadu
P.O. Box 48
57013 Oreokastvo
Thessaloniki
Greece
☎ +30 31 696 460

Hong Kong
Society for the Welfare of the
Autistic Person
Room 210-214, Block 19
Shek Kip Mei Estate
Kowloon, Hong Kong
☎ +852 2788 3326
fax +852 2788 1414
swap@swap.org.hk

Hungary
Autism Foundation
Delej U. 24-26
Budapest 1089
Hungary
☎ +36 1 314 2859
fax +36 1 210.4364

Autism Research Group*
Delej u. 24-26
H - 1089 Budapest
Hungary
☎ +36 1 114 2859
Dr Anna Balazcs

Iceland
Limsjonarfelag Eihverfe (Autistic
Society of Iceland)*
Fellsmuli 26
108 Reykjavik
Iceland
☎ +354 1 588 1599
fax +354 1 568 5585

India
Action for Autism
T- 370F Chiragh Gaon
Third Floor
New Delhi - 110017
India
☎ +91 11 641 6469
fax +91 11 641 6470
autism@vsnl.com

Ireland
Irish Society for Autism*
Unity Building, 16/17 Lower
O'Connell St.
Dublin 1
Republic of Ireland
☎ +353 1 874 4684
fax +35 51 874 4224

Israel
Israeli Society for Autistic Children
PO Box 32097
Tel Aviv 61320
Israel
☎ +972 (0)323 4965

Italy
Associazione Nazionale Genitori
Soggetti Autistici*
c/o Mr Sergio Martone
Via Rota 75
1 - 80067 Sorreno (NA)
Italy
☎ +39 51 6343 367

Associazione Italiana Per La
Ricerca Sulla Psicosi E L'Autismo*

Via des Mascherino 90
I - 00193 Roma
Italy
☎ +39 6 628 0728

Associazione Parenti Ed Amici Dei
Malati Di Autismo*
c/o P.A.M.A.P.I.
Scuola "Amerigo Vespucci"
Via Bolognese 238
I - 50139 Firenze
Italy
☎ +39 5 540 0594

Associazione Per La Ricerca
Italiana Sulla Sindrome Di Down,
L'Autismo E Il Danno Cerebrale*
c/o ANFFAS
Via Rasi, 14,
40127 Bologna
Italy
☎ +39 51 249 572

ANFFAS (Coordinatmento
Interventi Autis mo)*
Contact: Marco Chistolini
Via Carlo Bazzi, 68
20141 Milano
Italy
☎ +39 2 8950 0928
Fax: +39 2 8951 5740

Autismo Italia
Via del Serragtio 38
1-59100 Prato
Italy
☎ +39 0574 433 807
fax +39 0574 617 308
giavivan@boxl.tin.it

Japan
The Autism Society Japan
c/o National Welfare Foundation
for Disabled Children
2-2-8 Nishi-Waseda
Shinjuku-ku,

Tokyo, 162
Japan
☎ +03 3232 6478
fax +03 5273 8438

Kuwait
Kuwait Centre for Autism
P.O. Box 33425
Rawda 73455
Kuwait
☎ +965 2540351
fax +965 2540247

Luxembourg
Autisme Luxembourg a.s.b.i*
36c Cite Patton
L - 9068 Etterbruck
Luxembourg
☎ +352 458 009
fax +352 811 246

Malaysia
The National Autistic Society of
Malaysia
3rd Floor
Bank Rakyat Building,
140 Jalan Ipoh,
51200 Kuala Lumpar
Malaysia

National Autistic Centre of
Malaysia
4 Jin Chan Chin mooi,
Off Jin Pahang
53200 Kuala Lumpur
Malaysia
☎ +60 3 422 3744
fax +60 3 422 3744

Malta
The Eden Foundation
Contact: Godwin Scerri
Bulebel
Zejtun ztn 08
Malta
☎ +356 665 260

Mexico
Centro Educativo Domus. A.C.
Calzada de la Viga 1225
Colonia Marte
Mexico, D.F.
08830

Centrol de Rehabilitacion y
Educacion Especial
(C.R.E.E.) Merida,
Yuc Col. Francisco I. Madero
Merida,
Yucatan
Mexico

The Netherlands
Nederlandse Vereniging voor
autisme*
Huizerweg 54
1402 AD Bussum, N.H.
The Netherlands
☎ +31 35 693 1557
fax +31 35 691 6205

New Zealand
Autistic Association of N.Z.
PO Box 7305
Sydenham
Christchurch 8002
New Zealand
☎ +64 03 332 1038
fax: +64 03 332 1038
m.s.whitworth@extra.co.nz

Niger
Association Espoir C.C.Pc
nº 31665 X Niamey R.P.
Boîte postale 11.509
Niamey
Republic of Niger

Gazeteer

Nigeria
Nigerian Autistic Society
Mrs H.V. Blankson
PO Box 7173
Wuse,
Abuja
Nigeria
☎ +234 0 9 523 6670

Norway
Autismeforeningen i Norge*
Box 118
Ksjelsaas 0411
Oslo 4
Norway
☎ +47 2218 0923
fax +47 2223 5700

Panama
Panamanian Society for the Parents
of Autistic Children
Apartado 6
141 - Zona 6, El Dorado
Panama

Philippines
Autism Society Philippines
Room 201 ML Building
47 Kamias Road
1102 Quezon City
Philippines
☎ +63 922 4116

Poland
The National Society for Autism*
c/o Mr. Tadeusz Galkowski
Stawki 5/7
00-183 Warsaw
Poland
☎ +48 2 283 13211 ext.51 or
+48 2 284 77100

Stowarzyszenie Pomocy Osobom
Autystycznym w Gdansku
ulica Kosciuszki 91. 4

80-421 Gdansk
Poland

Autistic Society of Lower Silesia
53-621 Wroclaw
Glogowska St., 30
Poland

Portugal
Associacao Portuguesa para
Proteccao aos Deficientes Autistas*
Estrada De Queluz,
9, Alto da Ajuda
1400 Lisboa
Portugal
☎ +351 1 362 3703
fax +351 1 364 6720

Romania
Asociatia Romana pentru Copli
Autisti (ARCA)
Jules Janssen
ICA
Germany
☎ +49 31 4493 4711

Russia
Dobro Association for Autistic
Children Care*
Kazarmenny per.,
4 Str. apart. 1-2
109028 Moscow
Russia
☎ +7 095 238 9737

Saudi Arabia
Jeddah Autism Centre
Al-Falsalya Women Welfare
Society
PO Box 1001
Post Code 21433
Kingdom of Saudi Arabia

Singapore
The Autistic Association
(Singapore)
Block 97C
Upper Thomson Road
05-10 Lakeview Estate (574329)
Singapore
☎ +65 323 0068
fax +65 323 3262

Reach Me Project
Autism Resource Centre
25 Peck Seah Street # 05-00
Singapore 079315
☎ +65 323 3258
fax +65 323 1974
rmpinfo@pacific.net.sg

Slovak Republic
Society for Helping People with
Autism (SPOSA) Solovakia*
Kratka 10
811 03 Bratislava
Slovak Republic
☎ +42 7 531 5 437

South Africa
Association for Autism
P.O. Box 35833
Menlo Park
Pretoria 0102
South Africa
☎ /Fax: +27 (0) 12 346 2376

Autism South Africa
PO Box 84209
Greenside 2034
South Africa
☎ +27 11 486 3696
fax: +27 11 486 2619
patsie@iafrica.com

South African Society for Autistic
Children
Private Bag X4
Clareinch 7740

Cape Town 8001
South Africa

Spain
Associacion de Padres de
Affectados de Autismo I Otras
Psicosis Infantiles de Biskaia -
Apnabi
C/. Pintor Guezala 1-2
48015 Bilboa
Spain
☎ +34 4 475 5704

Associacio de Pares amb Fills
autistes*
3, Carrer Puigblanc
Mataro (Catalunya)
Spain
☎ +34 3 790 3155

Associacio de Pares amb Fills
autistes i caracterials de catalunya*
(APAFACC)
C.Sant Antoni Ma. Claret
282, A, 2n.2a.
08041 Barcelona
Spain
☎ +34 3 43 51679/51404
fax +34 3 45 55335

Associacion Guipuzoana de
Autismo y Psichosis infantiles
(GAUTENA)*
Apartado 1000
20080 San Sebastian
Spain
☎ +34 4 32 15344

Asociacion Espanola de Padres de
Ninos Autistas*
Navaleno, 9
Madrid 28033
Spain
☎ +34 1 76 62222
fax +34 1 76 70038

Associacion Espanola de Padres de
Ninos Autistos de Burgos*
Calle Las Torres, s/n
SP - 09007 Burgos
Spain
☎ +34 47 23 9142

Federaction de asociaciones de
Padres Protectoras de Personas
Autistas del Estado Espagnol
Autismo-Espana
Avda. Comunidad Madrid 43
Las Rozas -28230
Madrid
Spain
☎ +34 1 637 7455
fax +34 1 637 7762

Asociacion Nuevo Horizonte*
Avd. Comunidad de Madrid, 43
Las Rozas - 28230
Madrid
Spain
☎ +34 1 637 7455
fax +34 1 637 7762

Association de Padres de Personas
Con Autismo de Burgos*
C/ Severp Pcjpa s/n
Calle Las Torres, s/n
SP - 09007 Burgos
Spain
☎ +34 47 239 182

Gautena
P.O. Box 1000
20080 San Sebastian
Spain
☎ +34 43 215 344
Fax +34 43 215 239

Federation Espanola de
Asociaciones de Padres de
Autistas*
C/Navaleno, 9
28033 Madrid

Spain
☎ +34 1 766 2222
fax +34 1 767 0038

Fundacio De Pares de Psicotics I
Autistes 'Mas Casadevall'*
Av. August Font
44 est. 3er
08023 Barcelona
Spain
☎ +34 3 212 4548
fax +34 3 453 0686

Fundacion Menela*
Avda Marques de Alcedo, 19
36203 Vigo
Spain
☎ +34 86 423 433

Sweden
Riksforeningen Autism*
Lena Andersson (Director)
Bondegatan 1D
S - 11623 Stockholm
Sweden
☎ +46 8 702 0580
fax +46 8 644 0288

Switzerland
Association Suisse Romande de
Parents d'Enfants Autistes et de
Personnes Interessees par
l'Autisme*
Hameau de la Fontaine 23
1040 Echallens VD
Switzerland
☎ +41 0 21 883 0083
fax +41 0 21 883 0084
autism.ch.f@bluewin.ch

Schweizerische Informations - und
Dokumentationsstelle fur
Autismusfragen*
(Swiss Association of Autistic
Children's Parents)
Petrus Kanisius - Grasse 21
CH - 1700 Freiburg
Switzerland
☎ +41 26 300 7748
fax +41 26 300 9749

Tanzania
National Association for Care of
Autistics (NACA)
PO Box 35062
Dar es Salaam
Tanzania
☎ +255 08 1220/410645
mutag@udsm.ac.tz

Turkey
Otizme Sevgiyle Blinichi Hizmet*
Moda Dr Esat Isik
Caddesi 116
Kadidoy - Istanbul
Turkey
☎ +90 216 418 0395
fax +90 216 302 5899

Ilgi Society for the Protection
Autistic Children
17 Sokak, No. 47/2
Bahcelievler
Ankara
Turkey
☎ +90 312 221 0694
fax +90 312 212 1996

United States of America
Autism Society of America
7910 Woodmont Avenue
Suite 300, Bethesda
Maryland 20814-3015, USA
☎ +1 301 657 0881
Free ☎ 1800 3AUTISM ext.150
http//www.autism-society.org/
jzaroasa@smart.net

Uruguay
The Uruguayan Autistic Children
Parents Association
Enrique Martinez 1195
Montevideo
Uruguay

Venezuela
Parents Association for Autistic
Children
Apartado 3455
Caracas
Venezuela

**The Worldwide Autism
Association (for people with
Autism)**
President: Ruth Hermann
Postfach 8052
Zurich
Switzerland

Gazeteer

Useful websites

There is huge amount of information about autism available on the web. However, much of it is now out of date, some of it is irrelevant and some of it is very dull.

Listed below are some of the sites the NAS visit regularly and consider useful, either because the information on them is otherwise hard to find or because they tend to be very up-to-date. This list does not infer that we recommend sites nor are implying a criticism of any sites not included. If you know of any others that you feel we should include or if you are setting up your own site, then please let us know.

Autism specific sites
www.oneworld.org/autism_uk/
Obviously we think this is a good pace to start. There are many UK based links listed on the NAS site.

www.autism-in-scotland.org.uk/
The Scottish Society for Autistism also has a site.

www.autism-uk.ed.ac.uk/
A UK-based site which primarily covers parental concerns.

www.spidernet.nl/~martijn_dekker/internaut/intro.spml
This site is maintained by volunteers and carries some of the mostup-to-date news stories on autism. Mainly American and largely designed for interest not research.

www.feat.org/
It is possible to subscribe to an autism newslist through this website, which is operated by the North Californian Autistic Society. Again the news is mostly US based.

www.familyvillage.wisc.edu/lib_autm.htm
The best thing about this site is the exceptional number of links they have managed to put together. Most of them are US based but should still be of interest.

www.autism99.org
Papers form the world's first internet conference on autism are still available at this site.

Treatments and approaches

www.healing-arts.org/children/autism-overview.htm
A good overview of the variety of treatments and approaches available.

www.billytommey.co.uk/
Billy Tommey was the two year old who gained much media attention in 1999, after being treated with secretin.

www.osiris.sunderland.ac.uk/autism/
Dietary interventions are also gaining a lot of media attention at the moment. To find out more try the Autism Research Unit at the University of Sunderland.

www.kessick.demon.co.uk/aia.htm
If you are still interested in allergy induced autism AiA.

www.gfcfdiet.com/
A very helpful website devised by a group of parents in America giving practical advice on how to implement a gluten-free diet.

www.iaba.net/
Applied Behavioural Analysis (ABA), a popular behavioural intervention used with children with autism. The Institute for Applied Behaviour Analysis website contains a great deal of helpful information.

www.peach.uk.com/
In Britain, the charity Parents for the Early Intervention of Autism in Children also work to promote the role of ABA, Lovaas and other forms of early intervention.

Websites for people with autistic spectrum disorders

www.staff.uiuc.edu/~bordner/ani/

Autism Network International is a self advocacy group run by and for people with autism. The group welcomes families but the focus is on individuals with the condition.

www.users.dircon.co.uk/~cns/index.html

This is a site designed by a university student with Asperger syndrome, specifically for students with autism and Asperger syndrome.

www.cando.lancs.ac.uk

Contains careers advice for disabled students.

www.mental-health.freeserve.co.uk

This site does not contain much information about autism but it does provide a chat room service for people with mental health needs. We know that many adults with high functioning autism or Asperger syndrome will experience mental illness and this is a good place in which to share your experiences.

www.aytistics.org

This is an excellent site for peer support, forums and self-help strategies. The site is maintained by people with autism and Asperger syndrome.

www.inlv.demon.nl/

These are a series of support lists and forums for individuals with autism and Asperger syndrome and related disorders.

Websites suitable for family members or children with Asperger syndrome

www.udel.edu/bkirby/asperger/

This site was set up by a parent who wanted to help her son. Most of the site is designed exclusively for people especially young people with Asperger syndrome, however sections are also available for the rest of the family.

www.onelist.com/subscribe/aut-partners
A mailing list available for partners of people with autism.

http://tqjunior.advanced.org/5852/autism.htm
A site designed for the whole family but probably most useful for those with young children. It has a lot of material for siblings.

Publishers of autism related titles

AHTACA, Brimble Hill School, Lyndhurst Crescent Park North, Swindon SN3 2RW, ☎ 01793 617426, fax 01793 420356

Book point (Souvenir press), 39 Milton Park, Abingdon, Oxon OX14 4TD, ☎ 01235 400 400 ext 580 (Souvenir press tel: 020 7637 5711), fax 01235 832068, orders@bookpoint.co.uk

Cambridge University Press, The Edinburgh Building, Shaftsbury Road, Cambridge CB2 2RU, ☎ 01223 325883, fax 01223 325959, ukcustserv@cup.cam.ac.uk

Connoisseur Videos, 10a Stephen Mews, London W1P 0AX, ☎ 020 7957 8957, fax 020 7957 8968

David Fulton Books, 2 Briton Close, Great Ormond Street, London WC1N 3JX, ☎ 020 7405 5606, fax 020 7831 4840, orders@fultonbooks.co.uk

Early Years Diagnostic Centre, 272 Longdale Lane, Ravenshead, Nottinghamshire NG15 9AH, ☎ 01623 430879, fax, 01623 794746, diagnostic-centre@sutherlandhouse.org.uk

Element Books, Unit 25, Longmead Industrial Estate, Shaftesbury, Bury, Dorset SP7 8PL ☎ 01747 851339, fax 01747 851394

Future Horizons, 720 N Fielder Road, Arlington Texas 76012, USA, ☎ 001 817 277 0727, fax 001 817 277 2270, edfuture@onramp.net

Gazelle Book Services, 39 Milton Park, Abingdon, Oxon OX14 4TD, ☎ 01524 68765, fax 01524 63232

Grantham Book Services, Issac Newton Way, Alma Park Industrial Estate, Grantham Lincolnshire NG31 9SD, ☎ 01476 541080 (other enquiries % 020 8741 3663), fax 01476 541061, order@GBS.tbsltd.co.uk

Hopeline Videos, 25 Enmore Road Putney, London SW15 6LL, ☎ 020 8788 2718, fax 020 8785 6345

Jessica Kingsley, 116 Pentonville Road, London N1 9JB,
☎ 020 7833 2307, fax 020 7833 2917, post@jkp.com, www.jkp.com/

John Wiley and Sons, 1 Oldlands Way, Chichester, West Sussex PO22 9SA,
☎ 01243 779777, fax 01243 843296, bgiacopa@wiley.co.uk

Kluwer Academic Publishers, Order department, PO Box 322, 3300 AH
Dordrecht, The Netherlands, ☎ 0031 786 392 392, orderdept@wkap.nl

Outset Publishing, Saffron House, 59/60 High Street, Battle, East Sussex
TN33 0EN, ☎ 01424 854 124, fax 01424 775 926

Oxford University Press, Special Sales Division, Walton Street, Oxford
OX2 6DP, ☎ 01865 267475, fax 01865 267782, brackenc@oup.co.uk

Paradogs, 206 Panther House, 38 Mount Pleasant, London WC1X 0AP,
☎/fax: 020 7833 1009

Random House Inc, 400 Halm Road, Westminster, MD 21157-4698, USA

Robert Hale, Bailey Distribution Learoyd Road, Mountfield Industrial
Estate, New Rommey, Kent TN28 8XU, ☎ 01797 366 9966,
customer services fax 01797 366 929, orders fax 01797 366 638,
orders@baileydist.co.uk

Routledge, Tayor & Francis Ltd, Rankine Road, Basingstoke, Hampshire
RG24 8PR, ☎ 01256 813000, fax 01256 479438

Southern Cross University Press, PO Box 157, Lismore, New South Wales
2480, Australia, nsearch@scu.edu.au

Winslow, Order Department, Telford Road, Bicester, Oxon OX16 0TS,
☎ 01869 244 644, fax 01869 320 040, winslow@dial.pipex.com

List of advertisers

Index

Feedback form

Please complete this form and let us have your comments and suggestions about the Handbook. This will be a great help in continuing to develop this as an autism related resource.

While we do take every effort to ensure that the information contained is the most up to date and accurate available, it is inevitable that there are occasions when this will not be possible. So, this form should also be used to correct entries as they appear or inform us of any new developments which could be considered for inclusion in the next edition.

Please detach and return the completed form to:

Publications Manager
The Autism Handbook
The National Autistic Society
393 City Road
London EC1V 1NG

Name ....

Organisation ....

Address ....

....

....

City...

Post code ....

Tel ....

Fax ....

Email ....

Comments (please attached further details where appropriate).

....

....

....

....

....

....

....

....

....

Please print your details below:

Name ....

Position ....

Date ....

Please send me details of the following:

☐ membership of The National Autistic Society

☐ fundraising

☐ volunteering

☐ general information pack

☐ publications catalogue

☐ schools and adult centres

☐ copy of the Annual Review 1998-99